color: *a guide to basic facts and concepts*

Robert W. Burnham · Comptrollers Division, Eastman Kodak Company

Randall M. Hanes · Applied Physics Laboratory, The Johns Hopkins University

C. James Bartleson · Research Laboratories, Eastman Kodak Company

A report of the Inter-Society Color Council Subcommittee for Problem 20:

Basic Elements of Color Education

color: a guide to basic facts and concepts

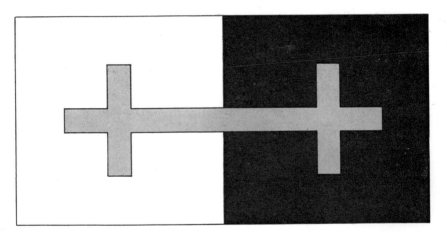

John Wiley & Sons, Inc., New York · London

Preface

In 1954 the Board of Directors of the Inter-Society Color Council accepted Problem 20 under the title "Basic Elements of Color Education" and appointed a subcommittee to study and report to the ISCC "a statement of the basic principles which should be included in any elementary teaching of color." This task has been interpreted to mean the preparation of a detailed outline of the facts, as distinguished from the *fancy*, of color. The job of preparing the outline fell equally to the three individuals whose names appear on the cover of this publication, after considerable consultation and clarifying advice from the subcommittee as a whole and from the Board of Directors of the ISCC.

The plan that evolved embraced several aims as follows.

1. To prepare a detailed outline of the facts of color in which each statement could (ideally) stand by itself out of context.

2. To code the outline in such a way that ready reference could be made to any part of it.

3. To document the outline with secondary published sources which are typically available in academic and industrial libraries and are themselves well documented with primary sources describing research on which the facts are based.

4. To cite primary sources whenever they are not already listed in the bibliographies included in secondary sources or whenever the

primary sources are not conveniently documented in secondary sources.

5. To adopt a set of color terms that conform as nearly as possible to common technical and commercial usage, but terms that are carefully defined and consistently used within the outline.

6. To include an index that refers to all color terms and concepts defined in the outline and of basic importance in the field of color.

7. To insert as many pictorial illustrations as are consistent with clarity and full communication, including as many color illustrations as possible, depending on excellence of reproduction and budgetary restrictions.

It was recognized that no outline concerning the highly complex subject of color, confined to simple statements of fact and stripped of expanded explanatory devices, could serve as a primer to the beginner. The final outline, therefore, is intended to fill three needs.

1. To serve as a course outline for an instructor academically prepared to teach a course in color.

2. To serve as a compact and reliable reference for a student who has *completed* a course based on the outline.

3. To serve as a basis for writing textbooks on color.

It should, however, be possible for an avid student to expand beyond the outline by going to the sources cited and reading extensively on his own.

This outline reports no new data, since it is simply a collection of existing items of knowledge. There is occasional novelty, however, in the organization of certain facts, particularly in the areas of color mixture, object-color systems, and color aptitude. Furthermore, a distinct attempt has been made to clarify confusing terms. Although any such attempt by a few individuals is doomed to relative failure (even before the task is begun), repeated attempts by many individuals may eventually accomplish the task we have set out to do.

Since facts vary in the firmness with which they are established, a point is reached at which it is sometimes difficult to separate fact from speculation or opinion. Nevertheless, an attempt has been made to present well-established facts or at least points of view on which there is broad general agreement. One serious danger in stating facts in the present form is that a fact typically represents an experimental result obtained under a particular set of laboratory conditions. Frequently the fact will be true only under those conditions and may not hold under more usual everyday conditions. Where facts must be limited, particularly in Chapters 3, 7, and 12, the reader should refer to the sources cited for amplification.

All sources, primary and secondary, are numbered in the bibliography in alphabetical order, and the numbers are placed at appropriate places in the body of the outline to document the statements made. Reference is made at the beginning of each chapter to general sources of interest in connection with the chapter.

Reference is made throughout the outline to other chapters or sections of chapters where related information may be found. These references are enclosed in brackets and coded with the outline code symbols which conform to a pattern as follows.

1.1
　1.1.1
　1.1.2
　　a.
　　　1.
　　　　a)
　　　　　1)
　　　　　　(a)
　　　　　　　(1)

References to a section are seldom as long as [1.1.2a.1.a)] but are more typically as short as [1.1.2a.], or even [1.1], or simply [1] where reference is made to a whole chapter. References to the bibliography are enclosed in parentheses.

The general plan of organization in the outline has been to proceed from an organized inventory of basic and relatively unquestioned facts, then to approved applications of certain important facts, and finally to a statement of marginal facts or facts on which there is less general agreement. To help clarify that plan, the outline is divided into three sections. Section I deals with the normal human stimulus-response system required for color and with the factors that modify color response. Section II deals with color-stimulus specification and facts related thereto; color-stimulus specification includes both measurement of the color stimulus and measures of color discrimination. Section III embraces the marginally factual but relatively unrelated areas of color vision theory, color aptitude testing, and experimental color aesthetics (an area in which there are large gaps in available color knowledge). A short chapter on color vision theory is included, not because theories are facts but because they help to integrate the facts of color and point the way to facts that need to be established.

Nothing has been said about color trends or "correct" applications of color because the *facts*, if any, are few and because there is no consensus among workers in these fields despite the volumes that have been written. If pet notions of the reader about color are not verified or included in the present outline, it may well be that, after all, he has been misled by reading *non*-factual exposés of color. The area of color aesthetics has been stripped to include only information that has been established through systematic research, painfully achieved, and a few "rules" that have stood the test of unsystematic but consistent experience. Though this stripping process may not appeal to the artistically minded, it nevertheless makes clear the difficulties inherent in establishing facts about the more complex affective aspects of human experience. Our task has been not to create beautifully phrased expressions of the many pleasurable ways in which color can be used and evaluated, but perhaps (hopefully) to extract the facts of color in such a way as to leave a clear implication of how *much* of color can be left to expressive judgment and how *little* of color has been factually established.

We would be greatly remiss if we did not attempt to express the depth of our gratitude to the many people who found the time in their busy schedules to read earlier versions of this report and offer constructive criticisms. Certainly the comments of V. K. Ball, Y. Galifret, R. W. G. Hunt, L. M. Hurvich, D. Jameson, W. E. K. Middleton, S. M. Newhall, D. Nickerson, H. Piéron, M. Richter, W. D. Wright, and G. Wyzecki are greatly appreciated. We have endeavored to utilize their advice, although they should in no way be held responsible for any of the statements included in this report. Through the efforts of L. M. Hurvich and D. B. Judd, comments by the American Psychological Association and Optical Society of America delegations to the Inter-Society Color Council have been solicited and made available to the authors. Again, although these criticisms have been greatly useful to the authors, our acknowledgment of the assistance of these groups should in no way be inferred to represent approval or sanction of this report or its contents by the respective parent associations. The original members of the ISCC Subcommittee for Problem 20, I. A. Balinkin, V. K. Ball, G. Brink, R. W. Burnham (Chairman), R. M. Evans, E. Faherty, C. E. Foss, W. C. Granville, W. N. Hale, R. S. Hunter, M. E. Jungerman, R. E. Pike, S. Wilson, and K. Yasko contributed much to the initial organization of the report, and many of them continued to offer constructive comments throughout the long process of writing and rewriting the actual report. Finally, a special debt of gratitude is owed R. M. Evans and D. B. Judd, who (together with C. J. Bartleson and R. M. Hanes) constituted an editorial review committee appointed by the ISCC Board of Directors in 1959 to recommend action on the question of the board's approval. These two acknowledged authorities carefully read and commented in detail on the entire report. Their comments and suggestions have been truly invaluable in the preparation of the final report.

To all those who have so kindly responded to our requests for comment and criticism, we are grateful. We have considered all their comments thoughtfully and usually have incorporated their suggestions. Still, we as authors must accept the responsibility for the report, since the final decisions and the forms by which we chose to express ourselves were ultimately ours alone.

We also wish to express our appreciation to Miss Ruth Ward and Mrs. Gretta Anderson for their excellent typing through many reworkings of the manuscript, and to Mrs. Pauline Fagan for her fine work in preparing the index.

Acknowledgment

The authors, on behalf of the Inter-Society Color Council, wish to acknowledge with appreciation the contribution of the Graphic Arts Research Department of Rochester Institute of Technology, Rochester, N.Y., which prepared and contributed all the color plates in this book. In particular, we wish to express our appreciation to Mr. W. L. Rhodes, director of that Department.

R. W. BURNHAM
R. M. HANES
C. J. BARTLESON

New York,
June, 1963

Contents

The Concept of Color

The concepts represented by the word "color" are and have been many and varied. Nevertheless, each of these concepts may be represented by some set of operations, either explicit or implicit.

In science and technology, operations of a given type may be repeated with more or less precision or agreement. In the observational operations corresponding to the term "length," for example, if the observer were to use many different rulers or measuring sticks, they would all be somewhat different in length and scaling. He would find that his repeated observations (measurements) of the length of an object would produce a number of different answers rather than a single, invariant point. The mean of this distribution would be his best estimate of the length of the object. Operationally, length can correspond only to the measurements made and the instruments used (31).

Fortunately, rulers or measuring sticks do not usually vary greatly, and repeated observations typically yield a narrow distribution of numbers so that the measurement can be said to be highly precise. This degree of precision is not always found in other measuring (observing) situations and, indeed, depending on the operations involved, may vary from exceedingly high to discouragingly low. The range of disagreement, or lack of precision, of observations represents a region of uncertainty which serves to cloud the meaning of the concept being examined. Meanings can be exact only where the region of uncertainty has been completely erased. This situation is never found, even in the most precise sciences.

In the early days of any science, its concepts are typically represented by words borrowed from everyday casual observation, and consequently their meanings are hazy and ambiguous. As the measuring (observing) tools and instruments develop in any science, results obtained with them are sharpened to a higher level of precision and the concepts represented by such measurements attain correspondingly higher precision.

Some of the operations represented by the word color, notably the more restricted, have enabled scientists to achieve a certain degree of metrical precision. In fact, much of the particularizing and restricting of color definitions that have been used from time to time may be traced to efforts to increase the precision of measurement. As a result of such efforts, however, much of the generality of meaning casually associated with the term color in everyday life has been deliberately forsaken.

Color is, first of all, a word that makes it possible for us to tell others something about what we are aware of when we look at the things around us. When we look at an object we may from time to time be aware of different aspects of the object, depending on what we have learned about the object and to what aspect of the object we are attending at the moment. Since workers in different areas of endeavor find different aspects of objects more interesting, there is always the tendency for any one interest group to define and particularize concepts in such a way as to make its own interpretations more easily describable and clearly understood. We have, then, a situation in which a single word, color, has been used to represent a number of different sets of operations. Different operations are implied by different users of the word, depending on whether they are interested mainly in chemistry, physics, psychophysics, psychology, art, or just plain conversation.

Let us say that a chemist has produced a sample of red plastic. He may say that its color is the result of certain characteristics of its molecular structure and that he can measure this color in a spectrophotometer, which automatically traces a curved ink line on a piece of paper. The chemist says that this ink line represents the color of the object. What he is aware of at the moment is not the red plastic sample itself but an inked line on paper, which nevertheless does represent some aspect of the object.

A physicist might protest and say that the curved ink line represents only the spectral reflectance of the red plastic, and that to represent its color this reflectance curve must be integrated with another curve corresponding to certain aspects of a light source (which sends out energy, which is then reflected off the sample). He says that this new curve represents the color of the sample. His scientific datum is a verbal report, color, representing his awareness of a curve different from the one the chemist was interested in.

The colorimetrist might still object that the color represented by either of these operations does not take into account the relation between the visual response of a standard observer and the so-called stimulus aspects of the object. In the science of colorimetry a great many years were spent deriving a precise operational concept of color which would represent a careful specification of operations performed. Color was operationally defined as that which is specified by a three-dimensional vector produced by manipulating numbers derived from measurements of radiant energy and from color-matching functions of a standard observer to an equal-energy spectrum. Mathematically these operations can be symbolized as

$$\text{Color} = (X, Y, Z)$$

and
$$(X, Y, Z) = f_i(E, R, \bar{x}, \bar{y}, \bar{z})$$

Color, in colorimetry, is a concept which means exactly what is represented by (X, Y, Z), and (X, Y, Z) is computed as a functional relation of energy (E), reflectance or transmittance (R), and the amounts $(\bar{x}, \bar{y}, \bar{z})$ of three arbitrary lights required to match each part in turn of an equal-energy spectrum for a standard observer. The colorimetrist, then, has gone beyond the chemist and the physicist by including in his concept of color the relations of a standard observer's response to both the spectral reflectance of an object and the incident energy in terms of the amounts of arbitrary (and not necessarily real) lights that the standard observer would mix to match the object under a fixed set of rigidly controlled (but not necessarily typical) viewing conditions. This operational definition of color is unambiguous and highly useful as a means of relating important spectral characteristics of objects to the response of a standard observer under set viewing conditions. It may not, however, be a very helpful definition for people who are interested in the *appearances* of objects.

The psychologist, and perhaps the artist, may say that such a specification represents an aspect of objects that is highly useful in some areas of science and commerce, but that there are other aspects of objects, possibly related to (X, Y, Z), which are of broader interest.

Color, they feel, should embrace these aspects. Beyond the self-imposed parochial limits of colorimetry, there are many interesting variations in the appearance of objects that have been the object of scientific investigation and practical concern. Depending on the viewing conditions, the surrounding objects or areas, the sizes and relative positions of objects, the adaptive state of the viewer, and a host of other things, a particular object that the colorimetrist characterizes by a given (X, Y, Z) can take on many different appearances. Some of these differences can be analyzed as differences in hue (redness, yellowness, greenness, blueness), saturation (dissimilarity of a given hue from a neutral of the same brightness), and brightness (the perceptual similarity of a hue-saturation combination to some one of a series of neutrals ranging from dark to light or dim to bright). The hues, saturations, and brightnesses that are abstracted from complete visual experiences and used to represent dimensions along which color may vary are functionally related to many things, among which are the spectral characteristics of the stimulating energy (E, R), the spectral matching functions of a particular observer $(\bar{r}, \bar{g}, \bar{b})$, the observer's memory (M) for similar objects, the surround (S), adaptive state of the observer (A), neighboring objects (O), the observer's attitude at the moment (T), and so on (u, v, w).

$$\text{Color} = (H, S, B) = f_i(E, R, M, S, A, O, T, \bar{r}, \bar{g}, \bar{b}, \cdots, u, v, w)$$

This generalization, which provides a broader basis for the concept of color, does not preclude the possibility of imposing restrictions and limitations in order to increase the precision of measurements. It merely tells us that whenever we impose such restrictions we may speak of color only within the context of the situation resulting from the restrictions. Whenever we remove the restrictions or change the conditions, our measurements will be partially or wholly inapplicable. Color, defined in this manner, more realistically represents all the operations entering into a given awareness of an object and is more nearly the concept used in everyday life and in research concerned with the appearances of objects. When most people talk about color they are referring to something they are aware of when they look directly at an object, to something that is one aspect of the direct visual experience of objects in general, an aspect of visual experience that can be referred to scales of hue, saturation, and brightness.

According to this last concept, color is considered an aspect of a complete visual experience apart from the spatial and temporal aspects of that experience. The myriad ways in which the non-spatial, non-temporal aspects of experience may change, depending on the spatial and temporal aspects as interpreted by the observer, may be dealt with in a straightforward manner using this concept of color. This definition of color, to be used in the present outline, is one that is frequently used (or inadvertently implied) in the modern literature on color. *Color, then, is defined as an aspect of visual experience* that may be referred to scales of hue, saturation, and brightness, comprising a three-dimensional complex apart from spatial and temporal aspects of visual experience. Awarenesses specifically of hue, saturation, and brightness may be abstracted from a total visual experience and scaled along these quantitatively specifiable dimensions of color.

These dimensions of color, hue, saturation, and brightness, do not comprise a *unique* coordinate system, for they may be related to other sets of coordinates that may be more practically useful, for instance, in routine colorimetry. They represent a cultural development upon which there is reasonably general agreement. Hue, saturation, and brightness may be judged separately along definable scales, each of which represents an abstraction from a total visual experience (which includes aspects of extent and duration as well as color). It is possible to abstract other non-spatial and non-temporal aspects of a visual experience for judgment, but in no way that is not describable in terms of combinations of hue, saturation, and brightness. Instead of judging "strength of hue" or saturation as such, an observer might be asked to judge "brilliance," which refers, operationally, to the degree to which colors "stand out" from the background. Brilliance may quite readily be abstracted from the total visual experience for judgment. Colors brighter (or darker) than the background, or colors contrasting because of high saturation, but typically colors combining both tendencies, will be judged more brilliant than others. The judgment of brilliance thus turns out to comprise a predictable combination of saturation and brightness.

Color scales are operationally defined in terms of the task set for a judging observer. For example, different intervals may be constructed along a saturation scale, depending on the judging task set for an observer. Instead of judging "equal strength of hue," an observer could be asked to judge "equal difference from a neutral of the same brightness." The first saturation scale is based on judgments of *equality*, while the second scale is based on judgments of *difference*, and they lead to different scales, which are, however, *not* independent; one bears a simple predictable relation to the other.

A distinct attempt has been made in this report to define a basic set of useful color terms and then to use them as far as possible with the same meaning. The difficulties inherent in such an attempt are particularly well known to semanticists. They have been clearly brought out in research on "the meaning of meaning" and reported in the literature. The problem of definition, specifically with respect to color terms, was dealt with recently by Graham (92) in a detailed report on color-vision theory. He pointed out how, even though a term has been defined, it may still take on different shades of meaning. For example, "color" may imply one thing in a verbal instruction to an experimental observer but have a somewhat different implication when used to refer to the experimental data recorded for the observer. Graham, as well as others interested in semantic problems, has suggested that, if all the possible shades of meaning could be determined, subscripts could be added to the term color (color$_1$, color$_2$, color$_3$, . . .) for use in different situations as a means of reducing the penumbra of uncertainty in any one case. LeGrand (93) circumvents the semantic problem completely by saying (p. 164): "The word colour is used in so many senses that it would be pedantic to attempt to give it a single meaning; the context should generally give the sense and, if there is any doubt, it is preferable to use another term."

Nevertheless, at the risk of being pedantic, we have defined color as comprising basic dimensions of hue, saturation, and brightness, since operationally these dimensions provide complete information about color as an aspect of visual experience apart from the remaining spatial and temporal aspects of that experience. If we now recognize that the word color, defined in this sense, still has different shades of meaning from one use to the next, we are at least making the careful reader aware of the fact that one simple word with a slightly penumbral meaning is permitted to serve for a possibly confusing half-dozen words with only slightly reduced penumbra of meanings. We believe that the more general definition can be successfully employed as a means of communicating with the audience for whom this outline is intended. Since the meaning we have given color is the one most generally implied in uncritical everyday communication, there will be the minimum necessity for adjusting old thinking habits to some special new situation.

Color, as defined here, implies a visual mechanism as a necessary basis for color, for without vision there would be no color. Color is a part of what we see, just as sound is what we hear. "Sound" is

defined as an element of experience. So it is with color. We do not
see energy or changes in energy, we see color—hues, saturations, and
brightnesses—and we certainly do not go about gazing at the world
through small apertures integrating all that appears therein. Limited
and controlled viewing conditions are vastly important in the systematic study of color, just as pure tones and anechoic chambers are
useful in the study of sound, but color and sound as parts of human
experience are not limited to these laboratory conditions. It is not
realistic, then, to attempt to discuss all the interesting aspects of color
that occur outside the laboratory—in everyday life—in terms of definitions that are deliberately formulated to exclude the kinds of variations in perception common to everyday life.

The concept of color as something that can be scaled along the
three dimensions of hue, saturation, and brightness does not exclude
or overlook the fact that any one object in any one setting may have
a number of different colors depending upon the observer's adaptation and attitude at any given instant. The point is that although
there may be a plurality of colors associated with a given object in a
given field, at any one instant in time each of these may be specified
in terms of coexistent three-dimensional complexes.

More restrictive definitions of color tend to accrue a plurality of
terms to cover these different appearances of objects. Such terms
are sometimes convenient and useful. There has been, for example,
considerable acceptance of the term "lightness" as a parallel term to
"brightness" when reference is made to an observer's estimate of the
relative luminance (luminous reflectance or transmittance) of objects. Such a term may be used to differentiate conveniently between
the fact that an observer perceives the absolute level of luminance to
be low but the relative luminance (luminous reflectance, for example) to be high, and we make some use of this term. Thus, an
observer may look at a piece of white paper which is obviously partially shaded and report that although the lightness of the paper is
high, its brightness is low. This is fine, as far as it goes. But there
are more than two different kinds of appearance that this same paper
can have in the same setting. The addition of the term "lightness"
to our color lexicon should not be taken to indicate that four perceptual terms (hue, saturation, brightness, and lightness) are sufficient to describe the perception of all colors in all modes of appearance. This, of course, is far from the truth.

The point is that any given object or medium may have many
different appearances even under exactly the same physical condi-

tions depending on the attitude, experience, and subtle perceptual factors of a given observer. It is important that *all* the factors in any expression for color be specified if a general expression for color is to be highly meaningful. Thus, we have defined color in a general perceptual manner and have used the terms hue, saturation, and brightness to describe the dimensions of any given three-dimensional complex which may be used to represent a color perception. By so doing, we do not mean to imply that these dimensions are either unique or entirely specific. Rather, we hope to make clear that a given object may have many different colors, depending not only upon physical aspects of stimulation but also upon psychological and physiological factors.

The terms hue, saturation, and brightness are *generic* rather than specific. Their descriptive precision depends upon the amount of information that is given with them to describe the perceptual complex within which they represent dimensions.

The attempt to define basic terms for use in this outline has, then, been approached from a broad operational standpoint. Although the actual choice of terms may have been somewhat arbitrary in some cases, the concepts represented by these terms are *basic,* and there is nothing arbitrary about them. The purpose of reviewing and, where necessary, modifying existing terminology has been to enable us to adopt terms that seem generally useful for outlining the basic facts of color and can be consistently used throughout to imply very much the same meaning. It should be noted that color, as a noun, has been reserved as a shorter term for "color response" (or "color perception"), and is used as a noun only when color response is implied. Where there might be some question about the meaning of color, based on old habits of thinking, the expanded term color response or color perception is used.

Section I

Basic Facts

Chapter One

A Definition of Color

Color is the attribute of visual experience that can be described as having quantitatively specifiable dimensions of hue, saturation, and brightness.

1.1 Color is one aspect of visual experience which is, in turn, one aspect of experience in general.

1.2 Visual experience has basic attributes of *extent, duration,* and *color* [Fig. 1.1].

> **1.2.1** A total visual experience has a great variety of spatial, temporal, and color aspects, any of which may be abstracted from the total visual experience for a variety of specific purposes.
>
> > **a.** The spatio-temporal aspects of visual experience in general comprise the contexts in which colors are experienced [2.3.2d.].
> > **b.** The contexts in which colors are experienced are called the *modes of appearance of color;* they are aspects of a total visual experience *apart from color* [2.3.2e.].

1.3 *Color* may be considered an aspect of visual experience *apart from spatial and temporal aspects,* and a variety of aspects are related to it.

> **1.3.1** *Physical* aspects of a situation producing color comprise characteristics of the radiant energy that stimulates the eyes to

[1.3]

produce color; physical aspects of such a situation may also be called *color-stimulus* aspects [2.1].

1.3.2   *Chemical* aspects of a situation producing color comprise characteristics of the chemical components of such things as pigments and dyes that reflect or transmit light to the eyes to produce color [2.1.3b.2.].

1.3.3   *Physiological* aspects of a situation producing color comprise such things as electrochemical activity in the nerves that lead from the eyes to the brain [2.2].

1.3.4   *Psychophysical* aspects of a situation producing color comprise the relations between specific amounts and kinds of color stimuli and particular color responses [3, 5, 6, and 7].

1.3.5   *Psychological* aspects of color refer to awarenesses of color, that is, color responses made by an individual when his eyes are stimulated by radiant energy. They refer also to the interactions of these conscious responses with the individual's other conscious responses and behavior, which include such things as attention, memory, motivation, and emotion [2.3, 3.8, 11, 12].

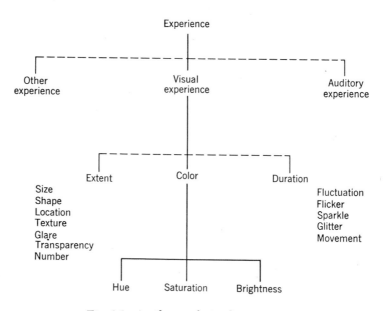

Fig. 1.1   Attributes of visual experience.

[1.3.5]

a. Basic color responses are awarenesses or perceptions specifically of *hue, saturation,* and *brightness,* which may be abstracted from a total visual experience and scaled along quantitatively specifiable *dimensions of color* [Fig. 1.2].

1. *Hue* is the dimension of color that is referred to a scale of perceptions ranging from red through yellow, green, blue, and (circularly) back to red.

a) A unit which has been suggested for the hue scale is the just-perceptible difference in hue, with the scale beginning at zero for some arbitrarily selected hue (such as a particular red).

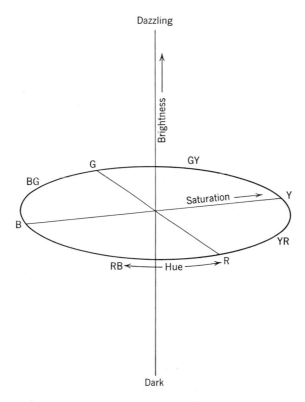

Fig. 1.2   Dimensions of color.

[1.3.5a.]

2. *Saturation* is the dimension of color that is referred to a scale of perceptions representing a color's degree of departure from an achromatic color (one lacking a distinguishable hue) of the same brightness.

   a) A unit which has been suggested for the saturation scale is the just-perceptible difference in saturation, with the scale beginning at zero for the achromatic color having the same brightness as the color to be designated.

3. *Brightness* is the dimension of color that is referred to a scale of perceptions representing a color's similarity to some one of a series of achromatic colors ranging from very dim (dark) to very bright (dazzling).

   a) A unit which has been suggested for the brightness scale is the just-perceptible difference in brightness, with the zero point a matter of arbitrary choice.

      1) The additivity of just-perceptible differences for brightness has been seriously questioned; for this reason, other brightness scales have been derived from direct appearance measurements (257).

   b) *Lightness* is a term frequently used in place of brightness to refer to opaque, reflecting objects seen in relation to other objects, and the scale ranges from black to white.

   c) *Lightness* is a term sometimes used in place of brightness to refer to transparent objects, and the scale ranges from black to clear.

   d) The colors produced by opaque objects, transparent objects, and light sources can all be scaled for brightness on the same basis. By disregarding (perhaps dramatic) spatio-temporal aspects of objects, a judgment can still be made in terms of similarity to some one of a series of achromatic colors ranging from very dim to very bright.

4. The *color* (apart from spatial and temporal aspects) of an object may vary in hue, saturation, and brightness, but in no way that cannot also be described in terms of *combinations* of these three visually abstractable dimensions.

[1.3.5a.4.]

a) The term *brilliance* has been used to describe a striking aspect of color that is a visually abstractable combination of saturation and brightness.

b) Other terms that have been used to describe visually abstractable aspects of color which turn out to be combinations of saturation and brightness are: *dyer's brightness, strength, depth, shade, cleanness, tint, tone,* and *intensity.*

c) The aspect of color that includes hue and saturation, apart from brightness, is called *chromaticness.*

5. Many people have organized their color experiences along lines of hue, saturation, and brightness, even though they have not given formal names to the three variables.

a) Descriptions of color difference can be reduced to basic terms such as redder-yellower-greener-bluer, more saturated-less saturated, and brighter-darker [9].

6. Hue, saturation, and brightness, as dimensions of color, may be represented in a three-dimensional space with variations in brightness shown as distances along a vertical axis, variations in saturation as radial distances away from the vertical axis, and variations in hue as angular distances around the vertical axis [8.3.3] [Fig. 1.2].

a) The hue, saturation, and brightness dimensions of color represent a cultural development on which there is reasonably general agreement.

b) The hue, saturation, and brightness dimensions of color do not comprise a unique coordinate system, since they are related to other coordinate systems which may be more useful in specific practical situations.

1) In the *standard CIE system of color-stimulus specification,* certain psychophysical relationships are represented in a three-dimensional space as dimensions related to visual dimensions of hue, saturation, and brightness for a given viewing situation [6].

2) In systems of object-color samples, arrays of objects are ordered along dimensions related to visual dimensions of hue, saturation, and brightness for a given viewing situation [8].

[1.3.5a.]

b. What have been called the *aesthetic* aspects of color constitute one class of psychological aspects; they refer to interactions,
within an individual, between visual responses to patterns of
stimuli and affective or emotional responses to the patterns [12].

1.3.6 *Theoretical* aspects of color refer to the explanations that
have been proposed to account for the colors seen under a wide
variety of stimulus conditions [10].

Chapter Two

The Color Stimulus, Receptors,

and Response

Color is typically seen when a color stimulus acts on the receptors in the eyes and they in turn set off activity in the nervous system which ends in the color response (25, 27, 49, 50, 60, 67, 77, 78, 93, 100, 143, 150, 152, 158, 159, 187, 223, 224, 238, 242, 274, 276, 286).

2.1 *Color stimuli* represent the first steps in seeing color; color stimuli comprise the *physical* or *stimulus aspects* of a situation producing color.

2.1.1 A *stimulus* is considered to be any change in external or internal energy that gives rise to excitation of the nervous system sufficient to arouse a response in the person concerned.

a. An object, such as a colored paper that is seen or a sweet substance that is tasted, is often called a stimulus, but it is more properly called a *stimulus-object.*

1. *Object-color* is defined as the color perceived as belonging to an object.

b. Since energy interchanges progress serially from a stimulus-object toward the person being stimulated, stimuli can be more or less proximal, i.e., near the nervous system (or its higher "awareness" centers).

[2.1.1b.]

1. When a photographic flashbulb goes off, the radiated energy in space is the stimulus, the filtered light energy in the eye is a different but more proximal stimulus, and the activity induced when the light energy strikes the back of the eye is a still more proximal stimulus [Fig. 2.1].

2. "The" color stimulus, if it exists at all, is in the strictest sense the last energy exchange preceding an awareness of color.

2.1.2 The usual initial stimulus for color is light. *Light* is defined as radiant energy capable of serving as a color stimulus.

a. Light comprises one small part of the *electromagnetic spectrum* of radiant energy, which also includes radio and television waves, infrared rays, ultraviolet rays, x-rays, and gamma rays [Fig. 2.2].

b. Radiant energy is released in bundles or *quanta* which may

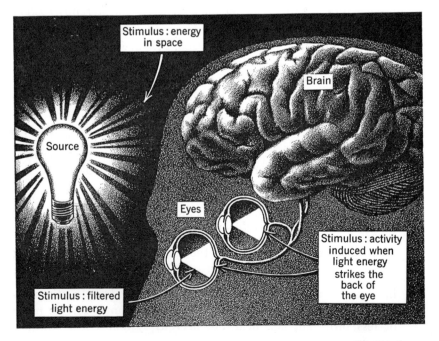

Fig. 2.1 Simplified diagram illustrating the successive nature of stimuli involved in a visual experience.

[2.1.2b.]

be thought of as traveling in waves of different lengths and heights but at the same speed, about 186,000 miles per second in air.

1. The quanta of light are called *photons.*

c. Light has numerous attributes, three of which are related to the role light plays as a color stimulus; these may be called

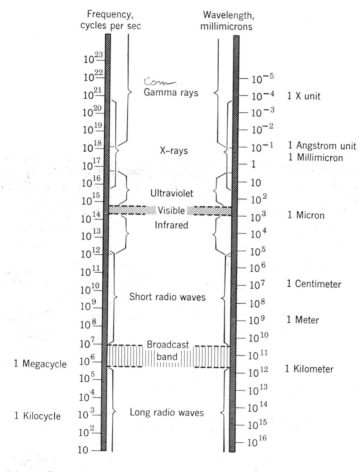

Fig. 2.2 A chart of the electromagnetic spectrum. From Sears, F. W., *Optics,* Cambridge (Mass.): Addison-Wesley Press, Inc., 1949 (3rd Ed.), Fig. 1-15, p. 21.

[2.1.2c.]

wavelength of single-frequency light, intensity, and wavelength composition.

1. One attribute of single-frequency light which is related to its role as a color stimulus is *wavelength*, which refers to the lengths of the waves in which light travels. Wavelength is usually expressed in millimicrons (millionths of a millimeter).

a) The shortest-wave light that ordinarily serves as a color stimulus has a wavelength of about 380 millimicrons (380 mμ), but under certain conditions light of wavelengths as short as 300 mμ may be visible.

b) The longest-wave light that ordinarily serves as a color stimulus has a wavelength of about 770 millimicrons (770 mμ), but under certain conditions light of wavelengths as long as 1000 mμ may be visible.

c) Light wavelengths generally are considered to lie between 380 mμ and 770 mμ; this range is called the *visible spectrum*.

2. A second attribute of light, whether of single frequency or of multiple frequencies, related to its role as a color stimulus is its (visually effective) *intensity*.

a) The intensity of light is related to the rate of incidence of the energy (in units of ergs per second) onto the visual receptor.

1) Light of any wavelength may flow to a receptor at different rates.

2) Typically, light of more than one wavelength serves as a color stimulus, so the intensity of the stimulus will depend on the rate of flow (radiant flux) at each different wavelength of the light comprising the color stimulus.

(a) For very short viewing intervals (less than about 0.01 second) the intensity of the color stimulus depends on the product of rate of flow and duration of the energy incident on the visual receptors. It makes no difference how this energy is distributed within the short time interval.

(b) For extended viewing intervals, the intensity of the

[2.1.2c.2.a)2)]]

color stimulus is determined by the rate of flow of the energy incident on the visual receptors.

(c) For a color stimulus simultaneously affecting small groups of neighboring visual receptors, the intensity is determined by the sum of the rates of incidence on each receptor separately.

(d) For a color stimulus simultaneously affecting large groups of neighboring visual receptors, the intensity is determined by the average of the rates of incidence on each receptor separately, that is, the rate of incidence on the whole group per unit area (expressed as ergs per second per square millimeter of retinal area).

b) To serve as a color stimulus, the intensity of light must be above a certain minimum (absolute threshold) [7.2.4b.].

3. A third attribute of light, related to its role as a color stimulus, is its *wavelength composition.*

a) A color response may be initiated by light of a single wavelength or frequency or by light of several or all wavelengths or frequencies in an infinite number of combinations.

d. None of the attributes of light is directly related to any single attribute of the color response, but wavelength of single-frequency light, intensity, and wavelength composition can be more or less indirectly related to color attributes by psychophysical relationships.

1. A psychophysical quantity which is related to the hue attribute of color is called *dominant wavelength.*

a) Dominant wavelength is defined as the wavelength of single-frequency light that can be mixed with light which appears white or achromatic to synthesize a stimulus that will produce the same color as some other stimulus.

2. A psychophysical quantity which is related to the brightness attribute of color is called *luminance.*

a) Luminance is defined as the ratio of the *luminous flux* (expressed in *lumens*) emitted per unit solid angle of a

[2.1.2d.]

source to the area of the source projected on a plane perpendicular to the line of sight [5.1.6c.].

3. A psychophysical quantity which is related to the saturation attribute of color is called *colorimetric purity*.

a) Colorimetric purity is defined as the ratio of the luminance of a single-frequency light to the luminance of a mixture of this light with "achromatic" light, such that the mixture produces a match for the color stimulus under consideration.

e. The *hue, saturation,* and *brightness* of a color response all depend to some extent on variations in *all three* psychophysical attributes of the color stimulus: dominant wavelength, luminance, and colorimetric purity [3.1].

2.1.3 All sources of light may produce color stimuli.

a. Some light sources produce energy that travels directly to the eyes to serve as a color stimulus; these sources are called *direct sources* or *self-luminous stimulus-objects.*

1. A solid or liquid that can be heated to very high temperatures will emit light when heated up to or above the point where it appears to glow; emission of light under these conditions is called *incandescence.*

a) The energy emitted by an incandescent source is distributed continuously over the region of the spectrum emitted.

1) The wavelength composition of the energy emitted by an incandescent source comprises not only waves in the visible spectrum but waves of greater and less length as well [Fig. 2.3].

(a) The wavelength composition of the energy emitted by an incandescent source depends on the temperature to which the source is heated [Fig. 2.3].

2) The common tungsten filament lamp is an everyday example of an incandescent source.

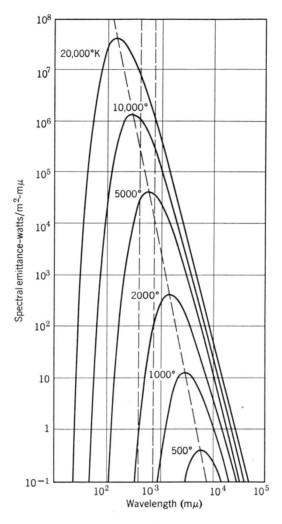

Fig. 2.3   Spectral emittance of a black body at various temperatures.   The vertical dotted lines indicate the boundaries of the visible spectrum.   From Sears, F. W., *Optics*, Cambridge (Mass.): Addison-Wesley Press, Inc., 1949 (3rd Ed.), Fig. 12-5, p. **315.**

[2.1.3a.]

2. Light may be emitted when the atoms or molecules of gases or vapors are excited by high temperatures, as in some kinds of combustion, or electrically, as in discharge tubes such as neon lamps. The emitted light results from activity in the individual atoms or molecules of the gas.

a) The light radiated by an excited gas or vapor is radiated at or near various characteristic wavelengths which appear as lines in the visible spectrum; the spectra produced are called *line spectra* [Fig. 2.4].

1) Since electronic interactions between elements in gases or vapors at low pressures are low, the emitted spectra are characteristic of the atomic structures of the elements; different gases thus produce different and characteristic spectra.

(a) Mercury vapor in a discharge tube produces a line spectrum, and the emitted light typically appears pale blue to pale green. These sources are used in street lighting.

(b) Sodium produces a line spectrum consisting chiefly of two bright yellow-appearing lines. Sodium discharge sources are used for highway lighting.

(c) Neon signs are a common example of self-luminous

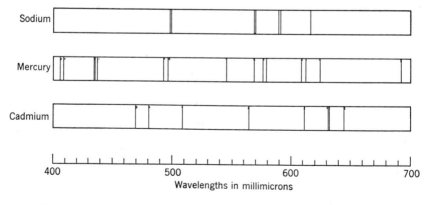

Fig. 2.4   Line spectra for sodium, mercury, and cadmium vapors.

[2.1.3a.2.]

stimulus-objects produced by an electrical discharge through gases.

b) In some flames and discharge tubes, radiant energy is produced by the excitation of molecules. This energy is radiated in discrete bands of wavelengths, and the discontinuous spectra produced are called *band spectra.*

1) An example of a light source having a band spectrum is the inner bluish cone in the flame of a Bunsen burner.

c) Some sources combine the two processes of continuous and discontinuous emission.

1) In mercury vapor lamps at low pressures, the emission spectra are essentially line spectra; at high pressures, however, a combination of continuous and discontinuous spectra results [Fig. 2.5].

2) An example of a light source combining continuous emission (from incandescence) with discontinuous or line emission is the carbon arc, where the light comes from both the incandescent electrode and from the flame of the arc.

3. Some self-luminous stimulus-objects may emit light without being heated; these are called *cool* or *luminescent* sources, and the light-producing action is called *luminescence* (in contrast with incandescence). Luminescence results from absorption of energy in various forms (electromagnetic, electron impact, chemical, etc.).

a) One form of luminescence is called *fluorescence,* which refers to the ability of certain substances (*phosphors*) to absorb energy and emit it, usually at longer wavelengths, after a negligible time delay (fractions of a microsecond); these substances are said to *fluoresce.*

1) The light emitted by fluorescent sources generally has a continuous spectrum (often with superimposed discontinuous spectra from discharges of gases included in the lamps); the spectral energy distributions are different for different phosphors [Fig. 2.6].

[2.1.3a.3.a)]

2) The common fluorescent lamp is an example of a fluorescent self-luminous stimulus-object.

3) Phosphors are used to produce fluorescence, not only in light sources but in cloth and paper to achieve brilliant colors in military signal equipment and advertising materials.

b) A second form of luminescence is called *phosphorescence,* a term which refers to the ability of certain substances to

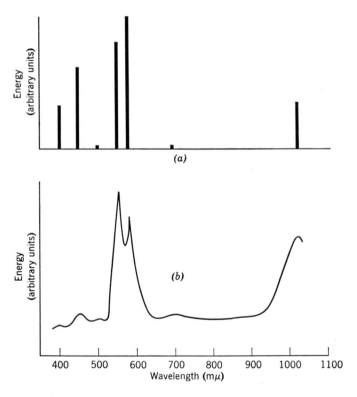

Fig. 2.5 Energy distribution in the spectrum of mercury vapor at (a) about 1 atmosphere, (b) about 100 atmospheres. The relative amount of energy at various characteristic spectral emission lines depends upon the pressure at which the gas or vapor is excited. In general, higher pressure results in more energy in the longer-wavelength lines and greater tendency to generate an emission continuum. From Murray, H. D., *Colour in Theory and Practice,* London: Chapman & Hall, Ltd., 1952, Fig. 3.4, p. 24.

[2.1.3a.3.b)]

continue to emit light long after the source of excitation energy has been removed.

1) Phosphorescent materials may be excited either by light or by other energy.

2) Some phosphorescent materials emit light for only a relatively short time, while others continue to emit light for many hours (sometimes as long as a day) after cessation of the incident excitation energy. The temporal dividing line between fluorescence and phosphorescence is arbitrary and ill-defined.

3) Except for a few special substances, phosphorescent materials emit broad-band or continuous spectra; the spectra emitted depend upon physical characteristics of the materials.

4) Phosphorescent materials are commonly used on objects that are intended to be seen easily in the dark, for example, watch dials and light cords.

c) Luminescence may occur as the result of *electrochemical, electrical,* or *mechanical* activity in certain substances and organisms.

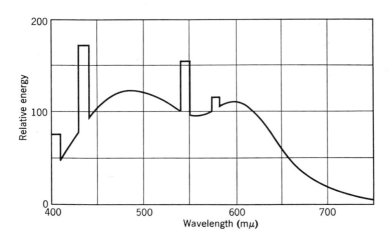

Fig. 2.6 Spectral-energy distribution curve for a typical fluorescent lamp. From Evans, R. M., *An Introduction to Color,* New York: John Wiley & Sons, Inc., 1948, Fig. 3, p. 29.

[2.1.3a.3.c)]

1) *Bioluminescence* refers to the capacity of some plants and animals, such as the firefly, to emit light.

2) *Electroluminescence* refers to the capacity of certain crystals to emit light when they are excited by electric currents. These crystals are important for "seeing-in-the-dark" devices and "wall" television.

3) *Photoelectroluminescence* refers to the use of light or other electromagnetic energy to create an electric current which, in turn, induces electroluminescence. Devices of this kind are the basis for modern systems of "light amplification."

4) *Triboluminescence* refers to the production of light by friction.

b. Although some light travels directly from the self-luminous source to the eyes to serve as a color stimulus, most light reaches the eyes indirectly from an object. Such objects are called *indirect sources* or *non-self-luminous stimulus-objects*.

1. When light is incident upon a non-fluorescent object or material, three things can occur. The energy can be *reflected,* *transmitted,* or *absorbed,* and usually all three occur, but the proportion of each is different and is often different at each wavelength [Fig. 2.7].

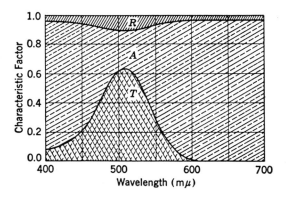

Fig. 2.7   Curves showing the reflectance (*R*), absorptance (*A*), and transmittance (*T*) of a substance dyed with a green dye. From Evans, R. M., *An Introduction to Color,* New York: John Wiley & Sons, Inc., 1948, Fig. 5.1, p. 59.

[2.1.3b.1.]

a) Non-self-luminous stimulus-objects may *reflect* part or virtually all of the light incident upon them.

1) The rate at which light is reflected by an object is always less than that at which it is incident upon the object.

2) Most objects tend to reflect greater proportions of light of some wavelengths than of others.

3) A particular object always reflects the same proportion of light at any one wavelength. This action results in a tendency to produce the same color response whenever the eye is adapted to the viewing conditions, whatever they are, and this tendency is the principal reason why color is often considered to be a property of objects, apart from their illumination.

4) The ratio of the rate at which light of a given wavelength is reflected from an object to the rate at which it is incident is called the *spectral reflectance* of the object.

b) Non-self-luminous stimulus-objects may *transmit* (let through) part or virtually all of the light incident upon them.

1) The rate at which light is transmitted by an object is always less than that at which it is incident upon the object.

2) Most objects tend to transmit greater proportions of light of some wavelengths than of others.

3) A particular object always transmits the same proportion of light at any one wavelength. This action results in a tendency, as it does for reflected light, to produce the same color response whenever the eye is adapted to the viewing conditions, whatever they are, and this tendency is the principal reason why color is often considered a property of objects apart from their illumination.

4) The ratio of the rate at which light of a given wavelength is transmitted by an object to the rate at which it is incident is called the *spectral transmittance* of the object.

[2.1.3b.1.]

c) Non-self-luminous stimulus-objects may *absorb* part or virtually all of the light incident upon them [Fig. 2.8].

1) The rate at which light is absorbed by an object is always less than that at which it is incident upon the object.

2) Most objects tend to absorb greater proportions of light of some wavelengths than of others.

3) A particular object always absorbs the same proportion of light at any one wavelength.

4) The ratio of the rate at which light of a given wavelength is absorbed by an object to the rate at which it is incident is called the *spectral absorptance* of the object.

d) An object that reflects or transmits the same proportion of light at each wavelength is typically called an *achromatic* object, that is, it normally evokes a color response in which there is no distinguishable hue; the object would be called either white, black, gray, or merely neutral; this condition is, however, not necessary for achromaticness, since some objects with spectrally selective absorptions may at times appear achromatic [3.9.2].

e) An object which reflects or transmits greater proportions of light of some wavelengths than of others is typically called a *chromatic* object, that is, it generally evokes a color response in which there is a distinguishable hue.

2. The study of the relationships between the chemical constitution of a non-self-luminous stimulus-object (colorant) and its absorption of light comprises the *chemical aspects* of a situation producing color.

a) *Colorants* are typically pigments (insoluble particles which most frequently produce light-scattering layers) or dyes (molecularly dispersed substances which most frequently produce transparent layers) which selectively absorb light of various frequencies and are classed as inorganic or organic chemical compounds.

1) An *inorganic* colorant is a chemical compound, typically not containing carbon as a principal element, in which absorption of light is often associated with the

characteristics of one or more of the ionic components of the compound.

(a) An example of an inorganic colorant is lead chromate, which typically appears yellow; other chromium-containing compounds may appear orange, yellow, or green.

2) An *organic* colorant is a chemical compound, typically containing carbon, in which absorption of light is produced by the peculiar structural arrangement of the components within the molecule.

(a) Most modern colorants are obtained through the synthesis of organic compounds.

(b) Until late in the nineteenth century, colorants were obtained almost exclusively from substances (both organic and inorganic) which, in their natural states, absorbed light selectively.

(c) The synthesis of organic colorants has provided the overwhelmingly largest number of colorants since 1856, when W. H. Perkin synthesized a reddish blue dye called *Perkin mauve* (287).

(d) The chemistry of organic colorants is a highly complex and specialized field which is principally concerned with analysis of chemical structure and synthesis to create new structures.

b) The systematic formulation of colorant layers is usually described in terms of physical (optical) characteristics of the colorant layers.

1) *Bouguer's law* states that, for a molecularly dispersed colorant of a given *concentration,* the transmitted flux (I_t) of single-frequency light of wavelength λ is a function of the incident flux (I_0), the extinction coefficient (a_λ), and the thickness (l) of the medium:

$$(I_t)_\lambda = (I_0)_\lambda \cdot 10^{-a\lambda l}$$

2) *Beer's law* states that, for a molecularly dispersed colorant of a given *thickness,* the amount of transmitted flux (I_t) of single-frequency light of wavelength λ is a func-

[2.1.3b.2.b)]

tion of the amount of incident flux (I_0), the extinction coefficient (a_λ), and the concentration (c) of the medium:

$$(I_t)_\lambda = (I_0)_\lambda \cdot 10^{-a\lambda c}$$

3) Beer's law and Bouguer's law may be combined to form an expression in which transmittance is function-

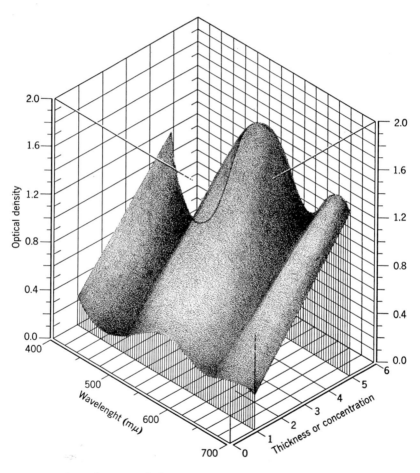

Fig. 2.9   Three-dimensional diagram showing graphically the relationship between wavelength, thickness or concentration, and optical density for dye. From Evans, R. M., *An Introduction to Color,* New York: John Wiley & Sons, Inc., 1948, Fig. 17.17, p. 267.

[2.1.3b.2.b)]]

ally related to the extinction coefficient, thickness, and concentration of the medium [Fig. 2.9]:

$$(I_t/I_0)_\lambda = 10^{-a\lambda lc}$$

4) Transmittance is not a convenient quantity to use in the study of colorants, since it does not vary in a linear manner with thickness or concentration; a related scale called *optical density* is frequently used.

(a) *Optical density* (*D*) is defined as the negative logarithm of the transmittance of a medium:

$$D_\lambda = -\log \frac{(I_t)_\lambda}{(I_0)_\lambda}$$

or $\quad D_\lambda = \log \dfrac{(I_0)_\lambda}{(I_t)_\lambda}$ [see Fig. 2.10]

(b) According to Beer's and Bouguer's laws, density (*D*) may be considered to be a direct function of the extinction coefficient (a_λ), concentration (*c*), and thickness (*b*) of a medium:

$$-\log \frac{(I_t)_\lambda}{(I_0)_\lambda} = a_\lambda lc$$

or $\quad\quad\quad D_\lambda = a_\lambda lc$

c) For transparent media the function of internal transmittance (T_i) that is sufficient to describe the stimulus aspect of a colorant resulting from its absorption of energy is merely

$$f(T_i)_\lambda = (D_i)_\lambda = \log \frac{1}{(T_i)_\lambda}$$

d) For completely opaque layers of pigment media the function that is sufficient to describe the stimulus aspect of the layers is called *spectral reflectivity* $(R_x)_\lambda$, defined as the spectral reflectance of a layer so thick that further increase in thickness fails to change the spectral reflectance.

e) For dyed and pigmented layers of paper or textiles, which both reflect and transmit light, the function of measurable

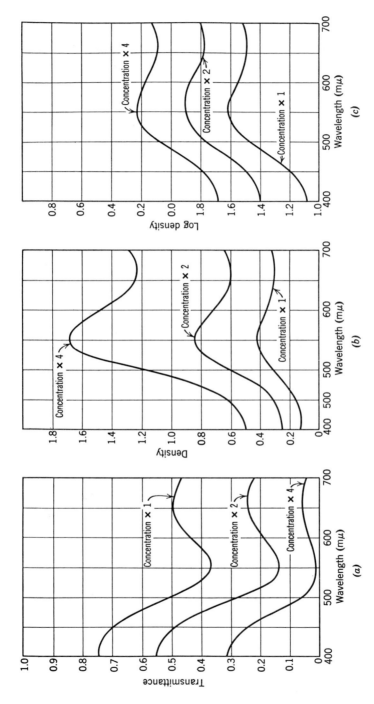

Fig. 2.10 The spectral characteristics of a solution for relative concentrations of 1, 2, and 4, shown in terms of (a) the transmittance at each wavelength, (b) the optical density at each wavelength, (c) $\log_{10}$ (optical density) at each wavelength. From Wright, W. D., *The Measurement of Color*, London: Hilger & Watts, Ltd., 1958 (2nd Ed.), p. 14.

quantities which is additive (in terms of proportions of the colorants involved in a given layer) and which is sufficient to describe the systematic formulation of the colorant layers may be analyzed by the Kubelka-Munk (159, 171) method, generally represented as:

$$\left(\frac{K}{S}\right)_\lambda = f(R_\infty)_\lambda = \frac{[1 - (R_\infty)_\lambda]^2}{2(R_\infty)_\lambda}$$

where K_λ = absorption coefficient,
S_λ = scattering coefficient, and
$(R_\infty)_\lambda$ = reflectivity.

1) The Kubelka-Munk analysis permits formulation of colorant layers by determination of the dependence of the scattering (S) and absorption (K) coefficients on wavelength; S and K are the respective sums of the scattering and absorption coefficients of the constituent colorant layers.

3. Non-self-luminous stimulus-objects may transmit or reflect light *diffusely*, without change in wavelength composition, or they may *scatter* light, with change in wavelength composition.

a) When light passes into a medium that contains large numbers of small particles differing in refractive index from the medium, the direction of the light that strikes each particle is changed. If the diameters of the particles are many times as large as the wavelength of the light and if the material of the particles is spectrally non-selective, the action of the particles themselves is also substantially non-selective, and there is essentially only a directional change; this action is called *diffusion* [Fig. 2.11].

1) Much of the light that is diffused within an object again reaches a surface of the object and leaves diffusely, so that the surface may appear almost uniformly luminous from all directions.
2) Light that is diffused by an object may be reflected or transmitted.

[2.1.3b.3.a)2)]

(a) When most of the light that is reflected by a surface is diffusely reflected, the surface is typically called *diffusing* or *mat*.

(b) When most of the light that is transmitted by an object is diffuse, the object is typically said to be *translucent*.

b) When light is not diffused by an object, the reflectance or transmittance usually is called *specular*.

1) Light reflected or transmitted by non-self-luminous stimulus-objects is usually neither completely specular nor completely diffuse but is intermediate between these extremes, that is, both specular and diffuse components are present [Fig. 2.12].

(a) Reflection that is principally *specular* is associated with objects having optically smooth surfaces, and these objects are typically called *glossy*.

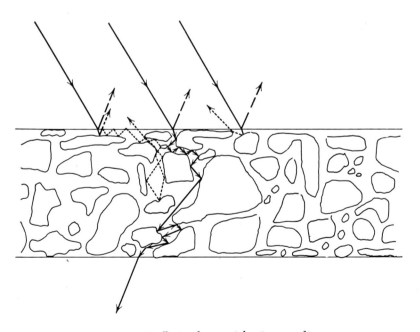

Fig. 2.11 Diffusion by particles in a medium.

[2.1.3b.3.b)1)]

>**(b)** Transmission that is principally *specular* is associated with relatively homogeneous media which are typically called *transparent*.
>
>**c)** Light passing through a medium that contains a large number of particles or other inhomogeneities may be *scattered* if the inhomogeneities are such that their minimum dimensions are approximately the same size as (or smaller than) the wavelength of the light.
>
>>**1)** Short-wave energy is scattered more than long-wave energy. For very small particles, light scattering is inversely proportional to the fourth power of the wavelength.
>>**2)** Scattering of light from the sun by atmospheric inhomogeneities is responsible for the blue appearance of the sky and is the reason why the sun appears red at sunrise and sunset [Fig. 2.13].
>
>**4.** Non-self-luminous stimulus-objects may cause *refraction, diffraction, interference,* or *polarization* of light.
>
>>**a)** The part of the incident light that is not reflected from the surface enters the object or medium and changes direc-

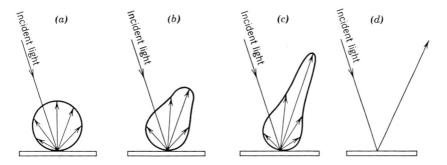

Fig. 2.12   The degree of optical smoothness of a surface determines the extent to which incident flux is reflected in all directions. A diffusing surface (as in *a*) tends to cause reflection equally in all directions. The smoother the surface (*b* and *c*), the more directional is the reflection until, with a perfectly smooth surface (*d*) all incident flux is reflected only at an angle equal to the angle of incidence.

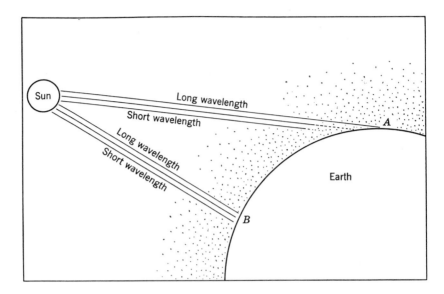

Fig. 2.13 Scattering by the earth's atmosphere. An observer at *A* is stimulated by relatively more energy in the longer wavelengths from the direction of the sun than is an observer at *B*.

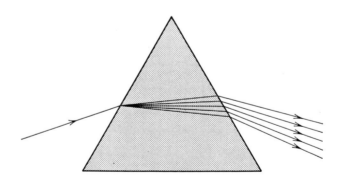

Fig. 2.14 Collimated light entering a prism is refracted according to wavelength, the shorter wavelengths being refracted more than longer wavelengths. The result is the dispersion of light into a spectrum. From Sears, F. W., *Optics*, Cambridge (Mass.): Addison-Wiley Press, Inc., 1949 (3rd Ed.), Fig. 2-28, p. 49.

[2.1.3b.4.a)]

tion or is "bent"; this bending is called *refraction,* and the amount of refraction varies with wavelength.

1) Refraction is the reason why a pencil in a glass of water appears to be "bent," and *selective refraction* causes the separation or dispersion of the various component wavelengths to form *rainbows* or the *spectrum colors* produced by a prism [Fig. 2.14].

b) *Diffraction* is the bending of waves around the edge of an obstacle. Diffraction results in the wavelength separation caused by interference patterns resulting from light passing through different parts of a small aperture or different points around closely spaced opaque objects [Fig. 2.15].

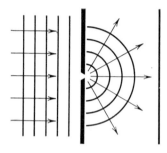

Fig. 2.15 Diffraction of light at a small aperture. When light waves pass through a suitably small aperture or past the edge of an obstacle, they are bent. The amount of this bending depends on the wavelength of the light. From Jenkins, F. A., and White, H. E., *Fundamentals of Physical Optics,* New York: McGraw-Hill Book Co., Inc., 1937, Fig. 3a, p. 53.

c) Whenever two waves of light from the same source combine there is *interference,* and this interference may be *constructive* or *destructive* depending on the phase relationship of the two waves; that is, the amplitude of the resultant wave may be increased by addition of the two waves or it may be decreased, even to the point of extinction, by cancellation of the two waves. Interference thus produces a redistribution of the light.

1) Interference may be caused by *refraction, diffraction,* or by *reflection* in thin films.

2) Interference films are sometimes used to isolate portions of the spectrum.

d) *Polarization* is a process by which some object causes the waves of light to be oriented in a given direction perpen-

[2.1.3b.4.d)]

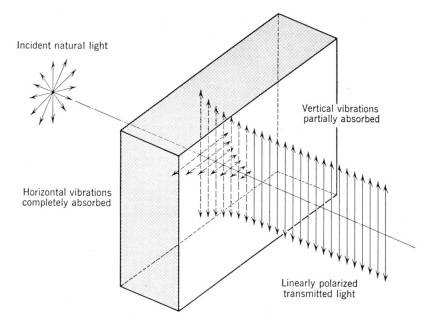

Incident natural light

Vertical vibrations
partially absorbed

Horizontal vibrations
completely absorbed

Linearly polarized
transmitted light

Fig. 2.16   Linearly polarized light transmitted by a dichroic crystal.   From Sears, F. W., *Optics*, Cambridge (Mass.): Addison-Wesley Press, Inc., 1949 (3rd Ed.), Fig. 7-13, p. 182.

dicular to the direction of propagation.   This may occur in certain crystals or other media by *reflection* or *scattering*, and by *transmission* through certain substances which have the property of polarizing light by *refraction* at two different angles [Fig. 2.16].

1) Polarization has several everyday uses, notably in certain sunglasses and in photography.

2.2   Activities induced by a color stimulus in the *receptors* of the eye and their attached *nerves* represent the second step in seeing colors and comprise the *physiological aspects* of a situation producing color.

2.2.1   The *visual receptors* are the parts of the eyes that are stimulated when light passes into the eyes; they are contained in the eyeball, which consists of several parts [Fig. 2.17].

[2.2.1]

a. The *sclera* is the tough white covering on the outside of the eyeball which gives the eye rigidity.

b. The *cornea* is an extension of the sclera and is the transparent area that protrudes at the front of the eye and allows light to penetrate the eye.

c. The *uvea* consists of three parts that line the inside of the sclera.

1. The *choroid* is a part of the uvea that lines the sclera over all the back and nearly up to the front of the eye. The choroid contains a great many blood vessels which nourish the eye.

2. The *ciliary body* is merged with the choroid near the front of the eye and contains three groups of muscle fibers which change the shape of the crystalline lens.

3. The *iris* merges with the ciliary body. It has a central cir-

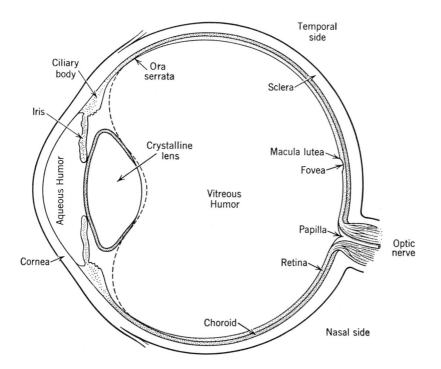

Fig. 2.17   Horizontal section of the eye (schematic).

[2.2.1]

cular aperture (*pupil*) which serves as the aperture stop of the eye.

d. The *retina* contains the light-sensitive elements of the eye [Fig. 2.18].

1. The retina lies inside the choroid and covers the rear two-thirds of the eyeball.

2. The retina contains a vast number of rod and cone receptors and nerves which are important for initiating conscious color responses.

2.2.2   The *optical system* of the eye, which directs incoming light through the eye to the point where the receptors may be stimulated, consists of several parts [Fig. 2.17].

a. The *cornea* is the first and principal lens in the optical system of the eye. It is primarily responsible for directing light through the eye to the receptors.

b. The *aqueous humor* is a clear, watery liquid (specific viscosity of about 1.03) which fills the frontal chamber between the cornea and the crystalline lens; it transmits light to the crystalline lens (64).

c. The *crystalline lens* lies behind the frontal chamber that holds the aqueous humor. The crystalline lens may be changed in form by the ciliary muscles so that images are clearly formed near the receptors regardless of the distance at which an object is observed.

d. The *vitreous humor* is a clear, viscous liquid (specific viscosity in the range of 1.8 to 2.0) which fills the rear chamber of the eye between the crystalline lens and the retina; it transmits light from the lens to the receptors in the retina (64).

2.2.3   The *receptor system* of the eye lies in the retina and consists of several parts, most of which are directly concerned with conscious color responses [Figs. 2.17 and 2.18].

a. The *ora serrata* is a thin irregular margin at the forward edge of the retina and represents the anatomical limit of the receptor system.

b. The *macula lutea* is a small area near the center of the retina which is somewhat thickened and yellow.

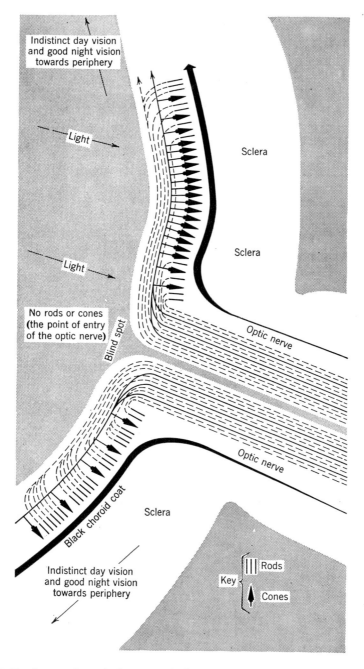

Fig. 2.18 Section through the retina (schematic). After Ruch, F. L., *Psychology and Life,* Chicago: Scott, Foresman & Co., 1953 (4th Ed.), p. 205.

[2.2.3]

c. The *fovea centralis* (*fovea*) is a very small, thinned-out area of the retina lying in the center of the macula; it contains no rods but has a very dense population of slender cones.

d. The *pigmented epithelium* is the outer layer of the retina (farthest from the lens) within which the light-receiving ends of the rod and cone receptors lie.

e. The *receptors* are usually considered to be the rods and cones that lie near the outer retina (just within the pigmented epithelium), and they contain chemicals sensitive to light (photochemicals) [Fig. 2.19].

1. The *rods* are spindle-shaped cells that are found only outside the fovea of the retina. They are sensitive to small amounts of light and are most useful at night when there is practically no color vision.

2. The *cones* are somewhat larger cells than the rods and are characteristically cone-shaped. They are, however, spindle-shaped in the foveal area where they are very closely packed.

f. The *blindspot* (*papilla, optic disc*) is an area of the retina outside the fovea where the axons of the ganglion cells [2.2.4a.2.] form the optic nerve and pass out of the retina to higher nerve centers; it contains no rods or cones [3.5.6].

2.2.4 The activity set off in the nervous system by activity in the receptors completes the physiological circuit needed to see colors.

a. There are two principal layers of nerves in the eye. They spread across the retina in front of the rods and cones, and light must pass through them to reach the rods and cones [Fig. 2.19].

1. The *bipolar cells* make up the first layer of nerves leading away from the rods and cones, but toward the front of the eye, and they are excited by activity in the receptors. Activity in this layer is passed on to the next layer of nerve cells at junctions called *synapses*.

2. The *ganglion cells* make up the second layer of nerves leading away from the rods and cones; activity in the ganglion cells is set off by activity in the bipolar cells. The ganglion cells

[2.2.4]

have long tails or axons which pass across the inner retina and out of the eyeball through the optic disc to form the optic nerve.

b. The *optic nerve* is a bundle of elongated axons of the ganglion cells, which passes on through several nerve centers [Fig. 2.20].

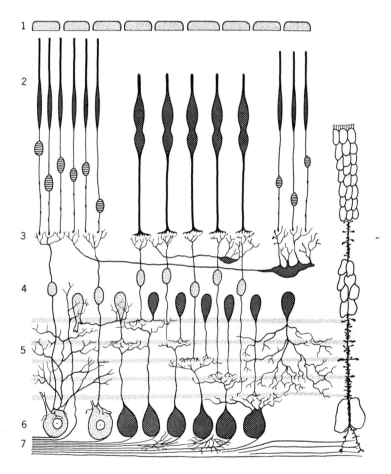

Fig. 2.19 The structure of the human retina (Greeff): 1, pigment layer; 2, rod and cone layer; 3, synapses; 4, bipolar cells; 5, synapses; 6, ganglion cells; 7, optic nerve fibers. After Cady, F. E., and Dates, H. B., *Illuminating Engineering,* New York: John Wiley & Sons, Inc., 1928 (2nd Ed.), p. 233.

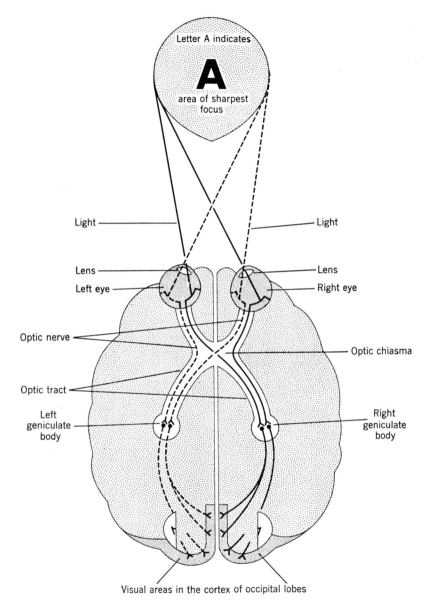

Fig. 2.20 The diagram above is a highly simplified presentation of neural patterns involved in seeing. At the top is the visual field, viewed from slightly different positions by the two eyes. Light rays, entering each eye through the lens, cross over to the opposite side of each retina. Nerve impulses then travel back to the optic chiasma where half of them cross over to the other side, with

[2.2.4b.]

1. The optic nerve bundles from each eye join and then separate again to form an "X"-shaped structure called the *optic chiasma.*

2. Beyond the optic chiasma, the optic nerves pass into "knee"-shaped structures called the *lateral,* or *external, geniculate bodies.*

3. There is a partial crossover of nerve fibers from the right and left eyes at the chiasma. All fibers from the right half of both retinas end in the right lateral geniculate body and all fibers from the left half of both retinas end in the left lateral geniculate body.

4. Activity beyond the lateral geniculate bodies is in another set of nerve fibers called the *optic radiations;* activity in the optic radiations is set off by activity in the ganglion cells of the optic nerve. Activity in the optic radiations is propagated to the *occipital lobes* of the *cerebral cortex* (outer part of the brain).

c. The *occipital cortex* of the brain is located at the back of the head and is the anatomical end of the nerve pathways related to color vision. When activity in the optic radiations reaches the occipital cortex, a conscious color response is produced.

d. Within the nervous system, the activity involved in producing a color response has certain characteristics significant for color vision.

1. There is a continuous spontaneous discharge in all nerve fibers, even when they are not stimulated by external energy.

---

the result that the right occipital lobe receives the impulses from the right halves of both eyes, reflected, in turn, from the left part of the object being looked at. By the same token, the left occipital lobe receives impulses from the left half of both eyes and from the right part of the visual field. How our nervous system can then organize these four separate sets of impulses into a unified perception is one of the great miracles of the human body. And somehow, too, our immediate and long-term motivational patterns enter into the picture to affect what we see. Actually, complex as this all is, seeing involves even still more, for there are other, smaller nervous "systems" active in opening and closing the lids of the eye, moving the eyeball in the desired direction, dilating and contracting the pupil, and lubricating the eyeball in its socket. All these functions are coordinated to make up the complex nervous reaction that we call vision. From Ruch, F. L., *Psychology and Life,* Chicago: Scott, Foresman & Co., 1953 (4th Ed.), p. 415.

[2.2.4d.]

2. The physiological effects of stimulating nerve fibers are superimposed on the spontaneous activity that is always present.

3. There are a variety of neural activities in individual nerve fibers.

a) There may be either increased or decreased electrical activity in a nerve fiber, as compared with the background or unstimulated level when a stimulus is applied.

b) A nerve fiber may respond to light with an initial burst of electrical impulses, which diminish in frequency while the light remains on; when the light is turned off this discharge stops.   This electrical pattern is known as an *on-effect*.

c) An *off-effect* shows a response pattern opposite to that of an on-effect.   There are no nerve impulses at all during illumination, but a vigorous discharge occurs when the light is turned off; this off-discharge usually subsides gradually.

d) There is a third electrical pattern in nerve fibers which combines an on-effect and an off-effect in direct succession; this is called an *on/off-effect*.   A short burst of impulses at high frequency occurs when the light is turned on, but after the initial burst there are no impulses at all as the light continues to shine steadily; another brief burst of impulses follows the "silent" period when the light is turned off.

4. Individual nerve fibers never act independently.   There is interaction among nerve fibers, and therefore visual function must be thought of in terms of the integrated action of all units of the visual system.

2.3 *Conscious responses* represent the third and final step in seeing colors and comprise the basic *psychological aspects* of *color*.

2.3.1 *Response* is the generic name for all behavior of the individual that results when some sense organ is stimulated.

a. Responses generally fall into three categories: motor, glandular, and conscious.

[2.3.1a.]

1. *Motor responses* are the responses made when muscles are activated.

2. *Glandular responses* are the responses made when glands are activated.

3. *Conscious responses* are awarenesses that result when the brain is activated.

b. *Color* is an abstraction from a visual type of conscious response which depends directly upon activity in the nervous system typically produced by stimulation of the retina by light [Fig. 2.21].

2.3.2 *Visual perception* is defined as the integrated conscious response to a total visual stimulus situation, but a response modified or interpreted in terms of the stored physiological remnants of past experience which are brought to bear in that situation.

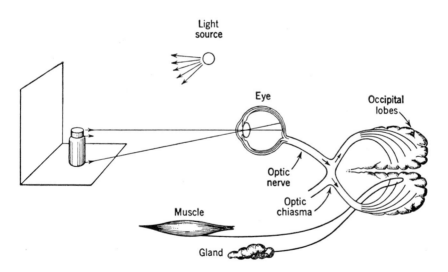

Fig. 2.21   Conditions required for the perception of a red object with a blue top. There must be a light source, an illuminated space, the object and its top, and an observer with at least approximately normal color vision. The formation of the retinal image, the cortical pattern, and the muscular and glandular patterns are also diagrammed. From Judd, D. B., *Color in Business, Science, and Industry,* New York: John Wiley & Sons, Inc., 1952, Fig. 11, p. 25.

[2.3.2]

a. Various aspects of a full visual perception may be abstracted for particular attention, and awarenesses of these various aspects are called respectively *color* perceptions, *form* perceptions, *movement* perceptions, *size* perceptions, *depth* perceptions, etc.

b. *Color sensation* may be regarded as the least complicated case or prototype of color perceptions, in the sense that it involves the least interpretation in terms of past experience.

c. A *color perception* may be specified in terms of the dimensions of hue, saturation, and brightness; color perception is thus equivalent to the term color, which implies awareness of the non-spatial, non-temporal attributes of a full visual perception.

d. Surface appearance, transparency, light-source appearance, glossiness, texture, flicker, glitter, etc., are spatio-temporal aspects of a total visual perception apart from color aspects; they refer to the spatio-temporal settings or contexts in which color is perceived.

e. Color perceptions are always only part of a full visual perception, and they occur in different settings or contexts which involve various forms and movements over a period of time; the various spatial and temporal contexts in which color is perceived comprise the *modes of appearance of color* [1.2.1].

1. There are five generally recognized modes of appearance in which color is perceived: *surface, volume, film* (or *aperture*), *illumination,* and *illuminant* [Table 2.1].

a) Color perceived as belonging to a surface is said to be perceived in the *surface* mode. A perception of this type is found in the presence of a spatially extended physical surface from which light is reflected; the stimulus-object is perceived as an object.

b) Color perceived throughout the bulk of a uniformly transparent substance is said to be perceived in the *volume* mode. A perception of this type is found where light is transmitted through a spatially extended liquid or solid of some finite thickness; the stimulus-object is perceived as an object.

c) Color perceived in space, where the stimulus-object is not distinguishable as an object, is said to be in the *film* mode. A perception of this type is typically found where viewing is through a small aperture, under conditions in which the

[2.3.2e.1.c)]

stimulus-object is not perceived as such and the color seems to fill the space behind the aperture.

1) The film mode of appearance is considered to be the simplest of all modes in the sense that it is the least removed from pure sensation.

d) Color perceived as light falling on objects is said to be perceived in the *illumination* mode. A perception of this type is found where there are in the field of view illuminated

Table 2.1 *Common Occurrence of Various Attributes of Visual Experience in Five Modes of Appearance*

Attributes of a Visual Experience	Illumi-nant (Glow)	Illumi-nation (Space-filling)	Sur-face (Ob-ject)	Vol-ume (Ob-ject)	Film (Aper-ture)
1. Color					
Saturation	X	X	X	X	X
Hue	X	X	X	X	X
Brightness	X	X	X	X	X
2. Spatial					
Size	X	*	X	X	*
Shape	X	*	X	X	*
Location	X	*	X	X	(Not in depth)
Texture	—	—	X	X	—
Gloss	—	—	X	X	—
Number	X	*	X	X	*
Transparency	X	X	*	X	X
3. Temporal					
Duration	X	X	X	X	X
Fluctuation	X	X	X	X	X
4. Spatiotemporal					
Insistence	X	X	X	X	X
Pronouncedness	X	X	X	X	X
5. Spatio-Color					
Lightness	—	—	X	X	—

Key: X indicates occurrence; * indicates only occasional occurrence; — indicates lack of occurrence.

Revised from S. M. Newhall, "Psychological Concepts: Perceptual and affective aspects of color," Ch. 5 in *The Science of Color*, Committee on Colorimetry, Optical Society of America, New York: Thomas Y. Crowell, 1953, p. 151.

[2.3.2e.1.]

objects which reflect light and cast shadows, whether the light source is visible or not; the color stimulus is not perceived as an object.

e) Color perceived as belonging to the source when a source of light is viewed directly is said to be in the *illuminant* mode. A perception of this type is found where a light source is present in the field of view; the stimulus-object is perceived as an object.

2. Recent studies have suggested a special case of the surface mode of appearance of an object when its luminance and purity are such that it does not appear to contain "gray" and does not appear to be a light source. Under such conditions an object may appear to be fluorescent (even though it may not be physically fluorescent). This has been referred to as the "fluorent" mode of appearance (70).

2.3.3 The psychophysiological processes of learning and conditioning are constantly producing conscious associations of color with various feelings, emotions, and meanings.

2.3.4 Although light is the normal visual stimulus, it is not the only means of initiating visual color responses.

a. Color responses can be produced by mechanical pressure on the ocular structures, chemical or physical irritation of the sensory fibers, electrical currents, powerful magnetic fields, certain drugs, certain diseases, and direct stimulation of the primary visual areas of the brain.

b. Color responses are produced by several different kinds of energy serving as stimuli, but they are also produced by more complex combinations or sequences of stimuli, which are more difficult to understand.

1. The stimulus for color may originate in the brain or nervous system, as it must in dreams or when an individual remembers colors.

2. Color stimuli that originate in the brain may result from a stimulus acting directly on an observer from the world about him which sets off more proximal stimuli derived from the stored but dynamic physiological remnants of previous experience [2.1.1b.].

Chapter Three

Variations in the Normal
Color Response

The color response in the normal observer can be affected by: energy variations in the color stimulus, spatial and temporal relationships within the stimulus field, the areas of the retina stimulated, the state of the observer's visual mechanism, and the observer's mental attitude (17, 49, 67, 93, 158, 159, 200, 292).

3.1 Variations in the energy characteristics of a color stimulus can affect the hue, saturation, and brightness of the corresponding response.

3.1.1 The intensity of the color stimulus is a factor in determining whether or not a color response is elicited and what the color will be; variations in intensity are associated principally with changes in the brightness of the color response.

a. When there is no light acting on a rested eye, it is not black that is seen but rather a dim color that may be interrupted by flashes of small colored dots. This is called *idioretinal light* and is caused by the continuous physiological activity in the eye.
b. Color, other than idioretinal, is seen whenever there is enough light acting on the eye to cause a response. The least amount of energy that evokes a visual response 50 percent of the time is called the *absolute threshold* [7.2.4b.].

[3.1.1]

c. As the intensity of the color stimulus is increased above the absolute threshold up to a certain level, all light except that of long wavelengths (beyond about 650 mμ) produces a brightness response essentially without hue or saturation. This energy range is called the *photochromatic interval*. The upper limit of this interval is called the *photochromatic threshold* [7.4.1b.].

> **1.** As the intensity of the color stimulus is increased above the absolute threshold, light of long wavelengths (above about 650 mμ in the visible spectrum) produces a reddish color of low saturation; in other words, there is no photochromatic interval for light of long wavelengths.

d. As the intensity of a small color stimulus with dark surround is increased above the photochromatic threshold, all hues are produced with progressively increasing saturation up to a certain intensity level; beyond that level (which varies with wavelength) saturation decreases, until again all hues disappear and only brightness remains (229).

e. Above the photochromatic threshold, the hues first seen for a given color stimulus will, with four notable exceptions, change as the intensity of the stimulus is increased. This hue shift is called the *Bezold-Brücke effect* [Fig. 3.1] (21, 230, 231).

> **1.** Stimulus-objects that produce orange or yellow-green hues appear yellower as the intensity of the stimulus is increased toward the level where saturation disappears.
>
> **2.** Stimulus-objects that produce purple or blue-green hues appear bluer as the intensity of the stimulus is increased toward the level where saturation disappears.
>
> **3.** Certain stimulus-objects that produce a unitary red, yellow, green, or blue hue continue to produce the same hue as the intensity of the stimulus is increased toward the level where saturation disappears. Such hues are said to be *invariant* with intensity [3.1.2a.2.].

3.1.2 Variations in the wavelength distribution of the color stimulus can affect the hue, saturation, and brightness of the color response.

[3.1.2]

a. The hue of a color usually (but not always) depends primarily on the particular wavelength distribution of the light acting on the eye.

1. The approximate wavelength regions of the visible spectrum (Table 3.1) ordinarily produce the hue responses indicated.

a) With isolated stimuli, wavelength regions associated with a reddish blue hue (380–470 mμ) and a yellowish red hue (595–770 mμ), when mixed in various proportions, ordi-

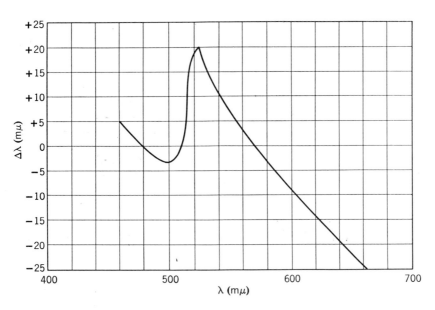

Fig. 3.1 Change of wavelength, at a fixed retinal illumination, producing the same change of hue as alteration from 1000 to 100 trolands (after Purdy), the radiation λ at 1000 trolands appearing the same as $\lambda + \Delta\lambda$ at 100 trolands; for example, the colors produced by light of 525 and 660 mμ at 1000 trolands would appear the same as those produced by light of 545 and 635 mμ at 100 trolands; the effect is thus very appreciable. On the average the fixed points are at about 571, 506, and 474 mμ. From LeGrand, Yves, *Light, Colour and Vision*, Fig. 59, p. 213. (Translated by R. W. G. Hunt, J. W. T. Walsh, and F. R. W. Hunt, New York: John Wiley & Sons, Inc., 1957.)

[3.1.2a.1.]

narily produce red (R), reddish blues (rB), red-blues (RB), and bluish reds (bR).

b) Attempts have been made to predict color responses quantitatively on the basis of wavelength relationships in stimulus configurations (124, 157).

2. There are four *unitary hues*, each of which has no resemblance to any of the other three. These unitary hues are called *psychological primaries*, and the wavelengths of light producing them are approximately those which retain invariant hue with change in intensity for a neutral condition of adaptation [3.1.1e.3.].

a) A "pure" red with no tinge of yellow or blue can be produced for an average eye by that mixture of light of 700 mμ and 400 mμ which is complementary to 495 mμ or by any light mixture having 495 mμ as its complementary wavelength [6.3.3c.1.c)1)(b)].

1) Under standard conditions, the light mixture which produces "pure" red varies with the observer; the mixture

Table 3.1   Typical Hue Names Associated with Spectral Energy Bands

Approximate Wavelength Region (in millimicrons)	Associated Hue	Abbreviated Hue Notation
380–470	Reddish Blue	rB
470–475	Blue	B
475–480	Greenish Blue	gB
480–485	Blue-Green	BG
485–495	Bluish Green	bG
495–535	Green	G
535–555	Yellowish Green	yG
555–565	Green-Yellow	GY
565–575	Greenish Yellow	gY
575–580	Yellow	Y
580–585	Reddish Yellow	rY
585–595	Yellow-Red	YR
595–770	Yellowish Red	yR

[3.1.2a.2.]

has been found to range from that having a dominant wavelength of 630 mμ, through the long-wave end of the visible spectrum, to that having a complementary wavelength of 521 mμ [6.3.3c.1.c)1)].

b) A "pure" yellow with no tinge of red or green can be produced for an average eye by light of 577 mμ or by any light mixture having 577 mμ as its dominant wavelength.

1) Under standard conditions, the light mixture which produces "pure" yellow varies with the observer; the dominant wavelength of the mixture has been found to range from about 568 to 583 mμ.

c) A "pure" green with no tinge of yellow or blue can be produced for an average eye by light of 513 mμ or by any light mixture having 513 mμ as its dominant wavelength.

1) Under standard conditions, the light mixture that produces "pure" green varies with the observer; the dominant wavelength of the mixture has been found to range from about 495 to 535 mμ.

d) A "pure" blue with no tinge of green or red can be produced for an average eye by light of 473 mμ or by any light mixture having 473 mμ as its dominant wavelength.

1) Under standard conditions, the light mixture that produces "pure" blue varies with the observer; the dominant wavelength of the mixture has been found to range from about 467 to 485 mμ.

3. As the purity of a stimulus (with a dark surround) is changed, there is primarily a change in *saturation*, but there is also a change in the *hue* of the color response; this hue shift which results from changing purity is called the *Abney effect* (1).

a) Addition of daylight to a field filled with spectrum light (with a dark surround) makes the hue of near greenish yellows approach greenish yellow but makes the hues of near greenish blues become increasingly different from greenish blue.

[3.1.2]

b. The *saturation* of a color is generally determined primarily by the purity of the stimulus.

1. The greater the purity of a color-stimulus, the higher is the saturation that is normally produced.

2. At moderate intensities of a single-frequency color stimulus, the highest degree of saturation is found for light in the long and in the short wavelength regions and the lowest degree of saturation for light in the region of 570 mμ [Fig. 3.2].

c. The brightness-producing capacity of light of different wavelengths varies from one wavelength to another.

1. The brightness-producing capacity of light of different wavelengths is usually measured by determining the amount

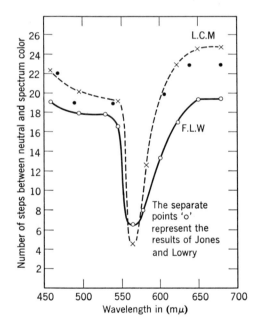

Fig. 3.2 Number of just-perceptible saturation steps between neutral and the spectral colors (for two observers [FLW and LCM]) using a 2° field. Color temperature of neutral, 4800°K. From Wright, W. D., *Researches on Normal and Defective Colour Vision*, St. Louis: The C. V. Mosby Co., 1947, Fig. 89, p. 162.

[3.1.2c.]

of radiant flux at each particular wavelength region required to produce the same degree of brightness as that produced by a standard.

2. The *luminosity function* is generally used to represent the relative brightness-producing capacity of light of different wavelengths.

a) The reciprocal value of the least amount of light at each wavelength required to produce equal brightness at all wavelengths may be plotted against wavelength to produce a graph of the luminosity function [Fig. 3.3].

3. In general, only small amounts of light in the middle wavelength regions of the spectrum are required to produce a brightness equal to that produced by much larger amounts of light in the long- and short-wavelength regions.

a) The diminishing abilities of light of relatively long and short wavelengths to evoke a visual response is the reason

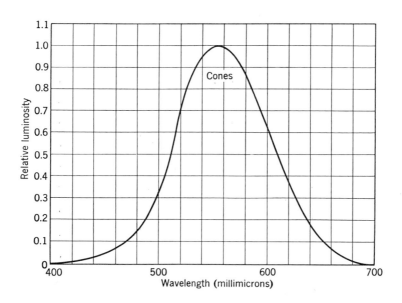

Fig. 3.3   Photopic luminosity function.   From Judd, D. B., *Color in Business, Science, and Industry*, New York: John Wiley & Sons, Inc., 1952, Fig. 2, p. 9.

[3.1.2c.3.]

why the wavelength range from 380 to 770 mμ is generally accepted as representing the spectral limits of light.

b) The range of light wavelengths from 380 to 770 mμ is the normal range beyond which visual response typically is insignificant; there are, however, instances where enough energy is available to produce color responses at wavelengths as short as 300 mμ and as long as 1050 mμ (102, 219).

4. The relative amounts of light at different wavelengths required to produce equal brightness at all wavelengths vary with the luminance level (below about 0.3 foot-lambert) to which the eyes are adapted. This change in the relative amounts of light required for equal brightness along the wavelength scale at different adaptation levels is called the *Purkinje phenomenon* and results from a shift from cone-functioning to more sensitive rod-functioning in the retina (247).

a) When an average eye is adapted to *photopic* (high) levels, light having a wavelength of about 555 mμ is found to have the greatest brightness-producing capacity [Fig. 3.3] [3.7.2b.].

1) Different wavelength bands of light can produce all the various hues seen at photopic levels of adaptation, except most of the red-blue hues.

b) When an average eye is adapted to *scotopic* (low) levels, light having a wavelength of about 507 mμ is found to have the greatest brightness-producing capacity [Fig. 3.4] [3.7.2a.].

1) Any light that serves as a visual stimulus at scotopic levels of adaptation produces indeterminate or greenish blue hues, regardless of the wavelength of the light (190).

c) When an average eye is adapted to *mesopic* (intermediate) levels, light of some wavelength between 507 and 555 mμ is found to have the greatest brightness-producing capacity, the particular wavelength depending upon the particular mesopic level and the corresponding ratio of cone- to rod-functioning.

[3.1.2c.4.c)]

1) As long as there is some cone-functioning at levels just above the photochromatic threshold, hues are visible, though not as many as there are at higher photopic levels.

3.2 *Spatial relationships* within the visual field can affect the hue, saturation, and brightness of colors.

3.2.1 Variations in the angular size of an object can cause a change in color, within limits, in much the same way as variations in the energy characteristics of the light coming from the object; this is called an *area effect* (35, 36, 109, 180, 256).

   a. The angular size, or *visual angle,* of an object is defined as the angle which the object subtends at the eye, regardless of the distance of the object.

   b. Up to a certain angular size (20 degrees or more under some conditions), the larger the visual angle subtended by an isolated object the more saturated is the color produced; beyond that

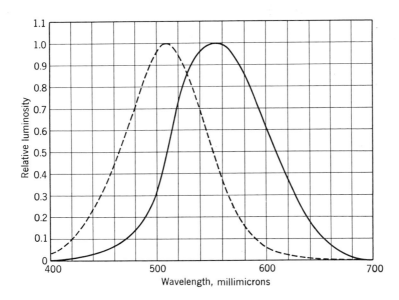

Fig. 3.4 Scotopic luminosity function (dashed line). Photopic curve is included for comparison. From Judd, D. B., *Color in Business, Science, and Industry,* New York: John Wiley & Sons, Inc., 1952, Fig. 2, p. 9.

[3.2.1]

size, the color becomes progressively less saturated [Fig. 3.5].
c. Up to a certain angular size, the larger the visual angle subtended by an isolated object the brighter is the color produced [Fig. 3.5].
d. Extreme size variations in a dark field produce marked brightness differences as a consequence of adaptation and contrast [3.2.2a.]. Under such conditions, a small patch can appear much brighter than a very large one of identical luminance.
e. Isolated objects of very small angular size (about 15 minutes or less) produce either a red or a green hue or some shade of gray from white to black when viewed directly (115, 184).

> **1.** Green-yellow or reddish blue distinctions fail with stimulus-objects of small visual angle; this effect has been called *small-area tritanopia.*
> **2.** Objects which produce a light green-yellow hue when they subtend a large visual angle, will usually appear light gray or white when their angular size is sufficiently reduced.
> **3.** Objects which produce a dark reddish blue hue when they subtend a large visual angle will usually appear dark gray or black when their angular size is sufficiently reduced.
> **4.** Objects which produce a blue, blue-green, or green hue when they subtend a large visual angle will usually appear green when their angular size is sufficiently reduced; further reduction in size will cause them to appear as some shade of gray, depending on the initial brightness they produced.
> **5.** Objects which produce a yellow-red, blue-red, or pink hue when they subtend a large visual angle will usually appear pink when their angular size is sufficiently reduced; further reduction in size will cause them to appear as some shade of gray, depending on the initial brightness they produced.

f. Isolated objects of the very smallest angular sizes produce no hue responses.
g. A reduction in color distinctions for objects of very small angular size has been demonstrated for both the fovea and the periphery of the retina.
h. Relatively dark objects in the far distance tend to look bluish, regardless of angular size, because of spectrally selective scattering in the atmosphere; relatively bright objects tend to look

orange or reddish because the light from them is scattered selectively.

3.2.2   The *position* of an object in relation to other objects within the visual field can cause color changes in much the same manner as do variations in the energy characteristics of the light coming from the object.

a. In general, there is a tendency for the visual mechanism to accentuate differences in objects juxtaposed either in space or in time.   This phenomenon is known as *simultaneous* (spatial) or *successive* (temporal) *color contrast* or *contrast enhancement* (81, 83, 101, 119, 130, 197, 221, 265).

1. Juxtaposed objects which produce high and low brightnesses generally appear respectively brighter and darker than they would if viewed with some separation either in space or time [Fig. 3.6].

2. Juxtaposed objects which produce colors of the same hue with high and low saturations generally appear respectively more and less saturated than they would if viewed with some separation in space or time; that producing the lower saturation may appear achromatic or even complementary to the color produced by the other [Fig. 3.7] [5.2.2a.3.].

3. Juxtaposed objects which produce complementary or nearly complementary hues generally appear more saturated than they would if viewed with some separation either in space or time [Fig. 3.8] [5.2.2a.3.].

4. Juxtaposed objects which produce non-complementary hues generally appear to be more different in hue than they would if viewed with some separation either in space or time [Fig. 3.9].

5. Because of contrast enhancement, large changes in saturation and brightness can be produced.

6. Sharp contours separating two colored areas tend to increase saturation and brightness contrast; poorly defined contours tend to reduce contrast [Figs. 3.10 and 3.11].

7. An object-directed attitude tends to reduce contrast enhancement.

8. A high brightness contrast tends to reduce hue contrast; equal brightness tends to maximize hue contrast.

[3.2.2]

b. In the case of certain complicated patterns, the changes that occur among the colors evoked by small, spatially juxtaposed areas are directly contrary to what would be generally expected as a result of contrast enhancement. They appear more alike rather than more different as in contrast; this phenomenon has been called a *spreading effect,* an *assimilation effect,* or a *color-mixture effect* (37, 128).

1. Small areas interwoven with fine black lines usually appear darker than the same areas interwoven with fine white lines [Fig. 3.12], at least partly because of lack of resolution or scattering caused by eye media.

3.3 Variations in *temporal* properties of the color stimulus can cause changes in the hue, saturation, and brightness of colors.

3.3.1 Stimulation by a steady light at a given intensity level results in a response that varies with time [Fig. 3.13].

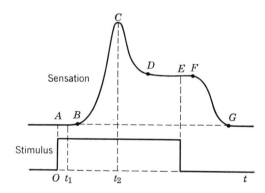

Fig. 3.13   Diagram illustrating the course of the sensation resulting from a constant stimulus.   Instead of beginning at *A,* at the same time as the stimulus, the sensation starts at *B* after a short delay (the latent period), then increases, passes through a maximum *C,* and subsequently falls again.   Then the sensation (except for a stabilized image) remains more or less constant at the level *DE.*   When the stimulus is removed suddenly, the sensation remains unchanged for a time *EF,* and then disappears progressively from *F* to *G.*   From LeGrand, Yves, *Light, Colour and Vision.* (Translated by R. W. G. Hunt, J. W. T. Walsh, and F. R. W. Hunt, New York: John Wiley & Sons, Inc., 1957, p. 300.)

[3.3.1]

a. There is a short latent period between the incidence of a color stimulus and the resultant color response.

b. Stimulation by a steady light is normally required for about 0.05 to 0.2 second to permit a color response to build up to maximum strength; this interval is called the *action time* (181, 216).

c. Brightness passes through a maximum during the action time for color; this phenomenon is called the *Broca-Sulzer effect* (32, 252).

d. Amount of rise, as well as rapidity of rise, of a visual response depends largely on the intensity of the color stimulus relative to the adaptive state of the eye [Fig. 3.14].

e. The time required for maximum saturation and brightness to be reached when the eyes are stimulated varies with the wavelength and intensity of the color stimulus (32, 215, 217, 252).

>   **1.** The time required for maximum saturation to be reached when the eyes are stimulated is somewhat less for red than for green colors and less for green than for blue [Fig. 3.15] (215, 217).

f. After a maximum color response is reached during stimulation with a steady light, there is a gradual decline in response level toward a steady state.

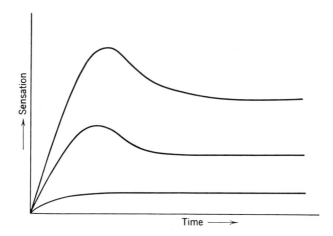

Fig. 3.14   Effect of intensity on growth of sensation. Upon stimulation, sensation grows more rapidly for higher intensity stimuli and except at lowest intensities "overshoots" before returning to a relatively stable level.

[3.3.1]

g. Investigations of vision with a stabilized image (one which is presented in such a way that it falls on the same part of the retina, irrespective of eye movements) show that eye movements are essential to normal vision, for it has been found that perception of pattern gradually fails for a stabilized image (61, 62, 233).

1. With a stabilized image, it is reported that the perception of pattern is at first normal but that the field gradually appears darker and sometimes even appears black.

2. Investigations of vision in which both eyes are presented with a *completely* textureless, formless image (referred to as a ganzfeld) have been found to lead to effects similar to those produced by a stabilized image in that the entire visual fields gradually tends to appear darker and achromatic regardless of the wavelength composition of the stimulating light.

3.3.2 When a stimulus that normally produces an achromatic response is presented intermittently at relatively low frequencies

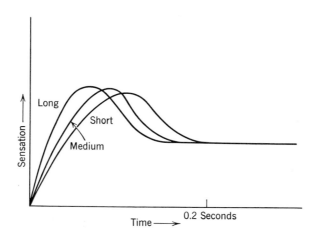

Fig. 3.15 Effect of wavelength on growth of sensation. The overshoot of sensation in response to stimulation reaches a peak at different times depending upon the wavelength of light. Long-wavelength energy produces a rise in sensation more quickly than short-wavelength energy. In general, the initial perturbations have been damped out within about two-tenths of a second for normal levels of stimulation.

[3.3.2]

(about 5 per second), chromatic sensations known as *Fechner's colors* or *subjective colors* are produced.

a. A great variety of Fechner's colors have been reported, ranging from graduated saturation of a single hue to a continuous sequence of different hues in regular spectrum order; these colors can be produced monocularly or binocularly, and they are typically of moderately low saturation (47, 82).

b. When a stimulus that normally produces an achromatic response is presented intermittently, it can produce brilliant orange and blue-green chromatic responses, but apparently only in binocular (not monocular) vision, at high levels of intermittent stimulus intensities, and at about 40 cycles per second; these responses are called *binocular subjective* colors and are indicative of interactions in the visual response mechanism (38).

3.3.3 Stimulation by intermittent light (within a certain range of frequencies of intermittence) produces a visual response of *flicker*.

a. When the eyes are stimulated by intermittent light, if the frequency of light and dark alternations is increased slowly from zero, there is at first no flicker response; then an early stage of coarse flicker develops which, with increasing frequency, becomes progressively finer until finally there is no flicker.

b. The perceived frequency of flicker produced by intermittent light differs from the physical flash frequency that produces it, especially as the frequency is approached at which flicker disappears (14).

c. The frequency of intermittent light at which flicker just disappears is called the *critical flicker frequency* (CFF) or *fusion frequency*.

1. The critical flicker frequency (CFF) varies widely with stimulus intensity, retinal area stimulated, state of adaptation, nature of surround illumination, and other factors.

a) In foveal vision, the CFF varies (for different stimulus conditions) from about 5 up to 55 cycles per second, and it is approximately proportional to the logarithm of the product of stimulus intensity and area. This relationship is called the *Ferry-Porter Law* (76, 227).

[3.3.3c.1.]

b) The CFF is higher in peripheral parts of the retina than it is in the fovea; this indicates that the fovea is less sensitive than the peripheral retina in perceiving intermittence or movement.

d. At high flicker rates (and above the CFF) the brightness produced by intermittent light is the same as if the total light flux entering the eye intermittently had been distributed uniformly over the whole period of intermittence. This relationship is known as the *Talbot-Plateau Law*.

e. At low flicker rates the brightness produced by intermittent light has been found to be as much as twice as great as the brightness produced by the same light presented continuously (17).

f. When flicker is produced by the alternate presentation of two stimuli that normally arouse chromatic responses (rather than by the alternate presentation of two stimuli of high and low intensity that normally arouse achromatic responses), there are two flicker components, one depending on differences in the intensities of the two stimuli and the other on differences in dominant wavelength and purity.

1. *Heterochromatic flicker photometry* is based on the fact that the CFF is higher for the brightness than for the chromaticness component of flicker.

a) The CFF for the chromaticness component of flicker is directly related to the differences in dominant wavelength and purity and to the mean intensity of the two stimuli that are alternated to produce flicker (85).

3.4 The after-effects of visual stimulation can result in a variety of colors which vary with the characteristics of the stimulus. These after-effects, which persist after the stimulus has been removed, are called *after-images*.

3.4.1 After-images are complex perceptions that can vary in hue, brightness, saturation, shape, pattern, texture, focus, latency, duration, and developmental sequence.

3.4.2 After-images are characteristically less objective and compelling than the perceptions produced by the original stimulus;

[3.4]

they are generally transient and filmy, and they drift and move with the eyes.

3.4.3 Simple after-images may be classified according to their appearance.

   a. After-images may be classified as *negative* or *positive*, according to the brightness relationships of the after-image as compared with such relationships in the original response to the stimulus.

     1. *Negative after-images* are defined as those in which brightness relationships are reversed compared with those found in the original response to the stimulus [Fig. 3.16].

       a) Negative after-images are more common than positive after-images.
       b) Negative after-images typically have a latency of about a second and a duration of about half a minute.
       c) The duration of the negative after-image can be increased by an increase in the pre-exposure through an approximate range of 0.05 second to several minutes.

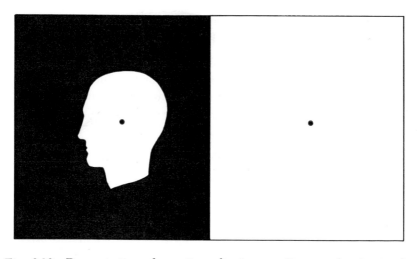

Fig. 3.16   Demonstration of negative after-image.   Stare at the dot in the white profile for about 30 seconds and then shift the gaze to the dot in the white square.   You should see a negative after-image in the white square; that is, a dark profile instead of a white one.

[3.4.3a.]

2. *Positive after-images* are defined as those in which the brightness relationships remain the same as those found in the original response to the stimulus.

   a) Positive after-images can be seen with practice after viewing a light figure on a gray ground under intense illumination.
   b) Positive after-images usually have a latency of only a small fraction of a second and may even merge with the terminal lag of the original sensation.
   c) Positive after-images are mostly flash-like in duration, but a type known as the *Swindle Ghost* variety may last for a minute or more (263).

b. After-images may be classified as *complementary* or *homochromatic,* according to the chromaticness [1.3.5a.4.c)] relationships in the after-image as compared with such relationships in the original response to the stimulus.

   1. *Complementary after-images* are defined as those in which each hue is approximately complementary to the hue of the corresponding location in the original response to the stimulus [5.2.2a.3.]; in a neutral field, this hue deviates from the strict complementary toward reddish-blue.

      a) The hue of the complementary after-image most closely approximates the complementary of the hue in the original response at moderate intensities and in a neutral field [Fig. 3.17]; in chromatic fields, the hue of the after-image depends on the chromaticity of the field.
      b) Some complementary after-images have a latency and a duration similar to those for the achromatic negative after-image, but others are most similar in these respects to the achromatic positive after-image.

   2. *Homochromatic after-images* are defined as those in which the hues are about the same as those found in the original response to the stimulus.

      a) Homochromatic after-images are produced by brief, intense stimulation.

[3.4.3b.2.]

b) Homochromatic after-images have a latency and a duration similar to those for the achromatic positive after-image.

3.4.4 Complex series of varicolored after-images, or after-image phases, can result from a simple stimulus of high intensity.

a. When the original stimulus is of high intensity and persists for several seconds or more, the resultant after-image series is called a *flight of colors* (19, 20).

1. A flight of colors is highly variable, can last up to 4 or 5 minutes, is characterized by successive image-phases numbering up to 40 or 50, with a progressive slowing and weakening of the image-phases.
2. The hues observed in a flight of colors are more dependent on the intensity than on the wavelength composition of the original stimulus.

b. When the original stimulus is of high intensity and of flash-like duration, or when it is moving, the resultant succession of after-images is known as *recurrent vision* (16, 251).

1. The phases of recurrent vision run their course in a few seconds.
2. Three phases of recurrent vision occur in the following order (200):

a) The *Hering image*, with a latency of about 0.05 seconds and a duration of the same order, approximates the original sensation in hue, sometimes merges with it, and is usually the brightest of the after-images.
b) The *Purkinje image* (Bidwell's ghost), with a latency of about 0.2 second and a similar duration, is often roughly complementary in hue to the original sensation and is next to the Hering image in brightness (153, 161, 162, 163).
c) The *Hess image*, which may last several seconds, is the lowest in brightness and distinctness and its saturation is relatively low. Any hue that is detectable approximates that of the original sensation.

3.4.5 Most people in everyday life do not ordinarily notice after-images, probably for two reasons: (1) we have learned to ignore

[3.4]

them because after-images tend to interfere with more useful perceptions, and (2) our eyes, through frequent shifting and movement, do not give them time to develop full strength.

3.4.6 After-images are important principally because of their implications for the functioning of the visual mechanism; they are one manifestation of the general process of visual adaptation.

3.5 Stimulation of *different areas* of the *retina* by the same light can produce differences in hue, saturation, and brightness.

3.5.1 Identical stimuli of relatively small size and moderate intensity can produce chromatic responses that differ in hue, saturation, and brightness in different retinal regions.

a. Except for stimuli of very small angular subtense, responses to stimulation of the central area of the retina are typically *trichromatic* [3.2.1e.] [5.3.1].

b. In general, responses to stimulation outside the central area of the retina are less clearly defined, less saturated, and more or less *dichromatic* [4.1.2].

c. In general, responses to stimulation near the periphery of the retina (roughly, more than 50 degrees from the fovea) are completely *achromatic* [4.1.1].

d. In general, visual responses fail completely for stimulation at the extreme periphery of the retina near the *orra serrata* [2.2.3a.].

3.5.2 Ordinarily, blue and yellow responses can be elicited by stimulation farther from the center of the retina than can red and green responses; these areas of different chromatic response are called *color zones of the retina* [Fig. 3.18] (8, 232).

a. The color zones of the retina are not sharply defined but vary with the state of visual adaptation and with the characteristics of the stimulus, particularly its luminance.

1. Chromatic stimuli which are very small or of very low intensity fail to produce chromatic responses as a result of stimulation anywhere in the peripheral retina.

2. Chromatic stimuli which are sufficiently large and of sufficient intensity can produce chromatic responses as a result of stimulation almost all the way out to the extreme periphery of the retina.

[3.5]

3.5.3 Light of certain wavelengths produces characteristic hues as far out in the retina as saturation is elicited; these hues have been called *invariable hues*, as distinguished from *invariant hues* [3.1.1e.3.].

a. There are three spectral stimuli (approximately 464 mμ, 489 mμ, and 571 mμ) that elicit respectively a characteristic hue in all areas of the retina.

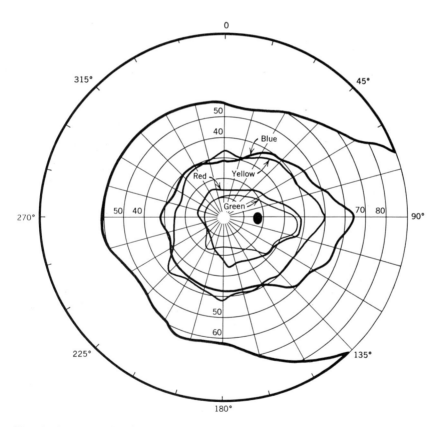

Fig. 3.18 Typical polar representation of the limits within which chromatic sensations resulting from stimulation by reasonably large, typically luminous stimuli are elicited in a right eye. From Committee on Colorimetry, Optical Society of America, *The Science of Color*, New York: Thomas Y. Crowell Co., 1953, Fig. 20, p. 104.

3.5.4 The same light can produce different brightnesses in different parts of the retina, but the differences will vary depending on stimulus intensity and adaptation level.

> **a.** A visual stimulus of sufficient intensity to evoke a response under *photopic* adaptation will generally evoke greater brightness when applied to the fovea than when applied to the periphery of the retina.
> **b.** Under *scotopic* adaptation, a visual stimulus of low intensity produces a far greater brightness when applied outside the fovea than when applied to the fovea, the central 2° retinal area being essentially blind at scotopic levels.

3.5.5 The effective energy distribution of a visual stimulus that falls within the macula lutea (yellow spot) varies as a function of the amount and distribution of yellow pigment within that area because of the selective absorption of light by the yellow pigment [2.2.3b.].

> **a.** The *macular pigment* extends over an area of 10 degrees or more in diameter around the fovea and varies in density, with the heaviest pigmentation occurring on the slopes and margin of the inner fovea.
> **b.** The extent and distribution of macular pigmentation vary irregularly and significantly from one person to another, and these variations can cause considerable individual differences in color vision.

3.5.6 In general, the area of exit of the optic nerve fibers of the retina (the *blind spot* or *optic disc*) is perceptually blind to any contrasting object that is imaged wholly within the area, but it is not blind to a uniform expanse of color or background imaged on a much larger retinal area that includes the optic disc [2.2.3f.].

> **a.** In binocular vision, "seeing" portions of each retina transmit impulses that "fill in" for the corresponding blind area in the other retina and so produce a visual response without blind spots.
> **b.** In monocular vision, the visual stimulus normally impinges on a retinal area larger than, but including, the blind spot, and the higher visual nerve centers literally "fill in" to create a visual

[3.5.6]

response without "holes" in the area corresponding to the retinal blind spot (277).

c. Although microscopic examination reveals no rods or cones in the blind spot, careful experimentation has shown some sensitivity there (122).

3.5.7 Specific stimulation of the retina near the fovea on the side away from the blind spot can result in the perception of reddish blue bands against a relatively dark background; this effect is called the *blue-arc phenomenon* (154, 196).

> **a.** The blue arcs may be seen in a relatively dark room when one looks slightly to the right or left of a vertical slit of light.
> **b.** The hue of the bands perceived in the blue-arc phenomenon remain blue or reddish blue regardless of the wavelength composition of the stimulus.
> **c.** The colored bands perceived in the blue-arc phenomenon have been ascribed to the electrical disturbance incident to the brainward passage of the optic impulses initiated by the parafoveal stimulus associated with the phenomenon.

3.6 Certain differences between monocular and binocular viewing can affect color responses.

3.6.1 The normal combination of the neural responses arising from stimulation of the two retinas in a single observer to produce a single visual perception is called *binocular fusion*.

> **a.** At ordinary photopic levels, a greater brightness is experienced when a given stimulus is applied to both eyes than when the stimulus is applied to only one eye (15).
>
> > **1.** The intensity of a stimulus acting on only one eye may have to be increased by as much as 50 percent to produce the same brightness obtained when the stimulus acts on both eyes at once.
>
> **b.** Although binocular, as compared to monocular, viewing of the same stimulus-object produces an enhancement of brightness, when corresponding areas of the two retinas are stimulated by different intensities binocular fusion produces a brightness intermediate to those obtained monocularly from the two

[3.6.1]

stimuli respectively. This apparent inconsistency is known as *Fechner's paradox*.

c. An achromatic response can be produced by binocular fusion of the effects of two stimuli that produce respectively a unitary red response in one eye and a unitary green response in the other, or a unitary blue response in one eye and a unitary yellow response in the other; fusion is difficult, but possible, under these circumstances.

1. Sometimes a yellow response, instead of an achromatic one, is produced in the binocular fusion of red- and green-producing stimuli, but this effect is reported to occur only with stimuli that separately produce a yellowish red or a yellowish green response [10.5] (145).

3.6.2 If (by means of a stereoscope or haploscope, for example) each eye can be stimulated at the same time with a very different color stimulus, the neural responses may fail to fuse, and there is typically an alternation of impressions from the two images known as binocular, or retinal, rivalry (213, 250, 262).

a. Sometimes, instead of discrete alternation in retinal rivalry, different parts of each pattern will be seen simultaneously in adjacent areas of the visual field, or there may be transparency effects.

3.6.3 The visual perceptions of most people tend to be predominately determined by the response of one of the two eyes; this is known as *ocular dominance* (9, 54, 55, 166, 186).

a. Ocular dominance can greatly affect the color that is temporarily perceived when the two eyes are stimulated by different color stimuli.

b. A marked ocular dominance will accent peculiarities of the functional eye.

3.6.4 Stimulation confined to one of the eyes is usually considered to have little, if any, effect on the sensitivity of the other (52, 90, 91), although some experimenters have reported that the sensitivity of one eye is slightly affected by adaptation in the other eye (5, 120, 121).

[3.6.4]

a. The brightness threshold for binocular vision is scarcely different from that for monocular vision (13, 220).

b. It is possible to adapt one eye to one source and the other to a different source and simultaneously compare the effects of these two illuminations on the appearance of color stimuli. This fact has been used to study color appearance [6.5].

3.7   Variations in the state of adaptation of the visual mechanism can affect color responses.

3.7.1   At any particular time, the visual mechanism is at some general level of sensitivity as a result of present and recent stimulation.

a. The overall range of visual sensitivity is from about 10^{-5} to 10^5 foot-lamberts, that is, a range of about 10 billion to 1.

b. At ordinary levels of stimulus intensity, the momentary range of visual sensitivity is of the order of 1000 to 1.

3.7.2   Whenever the visual stimulus changes, the visual mechanism starts adapting to the new stimulus.

a. *Dark adaptation* is defined as the general increase in visual sensitivity resulting from stimulation at an intensity level lower than that to which the eye has been adapted; when reference is made to very low levels at which only rod vision is operative, dark adaptation is often referred to as *scotopic adaptation*.

1. When an eye that has been thoroughly light-adapted at a relatively high intensity level is shielded from all light, cone sensitivity increases noticeably for only about 5 to 10 minutes, but rod sensitivity continues to increase for 35 minutes or more [Fig. 3.19].

2. The course of dark adaptation is affected by the previous adaptation level [Fig. 3.19] (45, 108).

a) Prolonged exposure to a high stimulus intensity retards dark adaptation.

b) Repeated daily exposure to strong sunlight reduces scotopic sensitivity so effectively that some of the effect can persist overnight or longer.

[3.7.2a.]

3. The course of dark adaptation is affected by the wavelength distribution of the light to which the eye was previously adapted [Fig. 3.20] (74, 239, 289).

a) For wavelengths less than 650 mμ, the longer the wavelength of the light to which the eye has been adapted, the faster is the rate of subsequent dark adaptation (133).

4. The course of dark adaptation can be affected by certain physiological factors (244, 245, 249).

a) Vitamin A deficiency and sometimes tobacco smoking interfere with dark adaptation.

5. The rate of dark adaptation is a function of the size of the retinal area that is permitted to adapt.

a) The larger the retinal area that is involved in dark adaptation, the higher is the rate of adaptation.

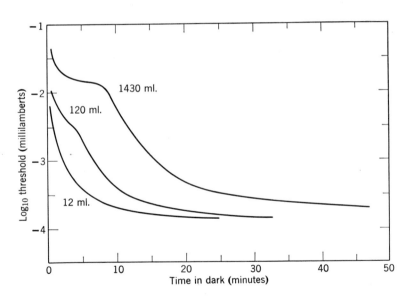

Fig. 3.19   Dark adaptation following 5 minutes of light adaptation to the indicated intensities.   (Monocular viewing with the natural pupil by one observer; circular test patch of 1.3° visual angle exposed for 1/50 second.)   After Winsor and Clark, *Nat. Acad. Sci.*, 22, 1936, Fig. 1, p. 402.

[3.7.2a.]

6. At the absolute threshold of the fully dark-adapted eye, all light (of wavelengths less than about 650 mμ) that produces any response at all produces either indeterminate hue or a desaturated, somewhat greenish blue hue [3.1.1c.1.] [7.2.4b.].

b. *Light adaptation* is defined as the general reduction in retinal sensitivity resulting from stimulation at an intensity level higher than that to which the eye has been adapted; when reference is made to the levels at which cone vision is fully operative, light adaptation is often referred to as *photopic adaptation*.

1. When an eye that has been previously dark-adapted is exposed suddenly to an illuminated area, sensitivity in the exposed area drops very rapidly (in a small fraction of a second) to a lower value, and adaptation is very nearly complete in a few seconds (240).

2. The course of light adaptation depends directly on the intensity of the adapting light and on the previous state of adaptation.

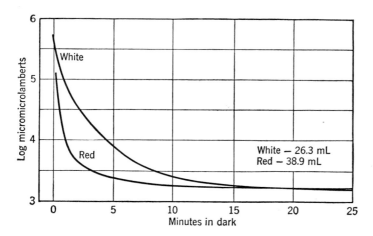

Fig. 3.20   Dark adaptation following preadaptation to incandescent light and to red light of about equal photopic luminance. It is clear that, following white preadaptation, dark adaptation (which here is purely rod) is slower than that following red preadaptation. (Hecht and Hsia, 1945.)   From Stevens, S. S. (Ed.), *Handbook of Experimental Psychology*, New York: John Wiley & Sons, Inc., 1951, Fig. 26, p. 951.

[3.7.2]

c. Adaptation has a significant effect on brightness.

1. If the eye is permitted to adapt fully to the intensity of the stimulus, there is relatively little change in brightness as intensity is increased.

a) Between about 1 to 100 foot-lamberts brightness increases with intensity if the eye is fully adapted to the intensity.
b) Above 100 foot-lamberts brightness increases, but slightly, with intensity if the eye is fully adapted to the intensity.

2. If the eye is not permitted to adapt fully to the intensity of the stimulus, the brightness of the visual sensation varies with the intensity within fairly wide limits.

d. Adaptation has a significant effect on brightness discrimination [7.4.2a.].

1. When the eye is fully adapted to the intensity of a photopic stimulus at a fairly high level, brightness discrimination is at a maximum.
2. Adaptation to stimuli above or below the test stimulus level reduces brightness discrimination at the test level.

e. *Chromatic adaptation* is defined as the general adjustment in spectral sensitivity of the retina when stimulated by a photopic stimulus that normally produces a chromatic response.

1. Chromatic adaptation to a given stimulus leads to variations in the color response to that stimulus (46, 127, 195, 204, 270).

a) As chromatic adaptation to a given stimulus progresses, there is a progressive decrease in saturation (rapid at first, then slower until an almost steady state is reached), and brightness shifts in general toward a middle value (except for stabilized images and ganzfelds [3.3.1g.1. and 2.]).
b) As chromatic adaptation to a given stimulus progresses, there is a complete loss of saturation in the response to a stimulus of low purity or to a small stimulus affecting the peripheral retina.

[3.7.2e.1.]

c) As chromatic adaptation to a given stimulus progresses, there are large hue shifts for stimulation of the peripheral retina, but no important hue shifts are found with central fixation.

2. Chromatic adaptation to a given stimulus can affect the hue, saturation, and brightness of responses to subsequent stimuli.

a) A stimulus that normally produces a neutral response will, following chromatic adaptation, produce a response in which the hue is nearly complementary to that produced by the adaptation stimulus before adaptation.

b) A stimulus that normally produces a response having a hue nearly complementary to that produced by an adaptation stimulus will, following chromatic adaptation, produce a response having a more nearly complementary hue of increased saturation.

c) A stimulus that normally produces a response having a particular hue will, following chromatic adaptation to a stimulus which produces initially a response of related hue, produce a response in which the hue is more remote from the related hue and is less saturated.

d) A stimulus which normally produces a response having a particular hue and saturation will, following chromatic adaptation to a stimulus which produces initially a response of the same hue but greater saturation, produce a neutral gray response if the spectral adjustive effect of the adaptation is just sufficient to cancel the saturation-producing capacity of the surface.

e) A stimulus which normally produces a response having a particular hue, saturation, and brightness will, following chromatic adaptation to a stimulus which produces initially a response of the same hue and saturation but much higher brightness, produce a complementary hue tending toward reddish blue (6, 157, 271).

f) In general, chromatic adaptation alters spectral sensitivity in such a way that the adaptation hue is suppressed in subsequent viewing.

[3.7.2e.]

3. Hue and saturation discrimination vary with chromatic adaptation in a manner similar to the way in which brightness discrimination varies with light adaptation.

a) In general, the more nearly the eye reaches full chromatic adaptation to a given stimulus pattern, the greater is the capacity to discriminate, by color, among the stimuli.

3.7.3 At any particular time under ordinary conditions, any given place on the retina is at some special level of sensitivity with respect to the general level of sensitivity.

a. Adaptation produced by a stimulus that has been confined to a specific, more or less sharply defined, region of the retina is called *local adaptation* (66).

1. Local adaptation is generally involved in the phenomena of after-images and successive color contrast.

b. The effect of local adaptation on adjoining areas of the retina has been called *lateral adaptation* (66).

1. Lateral adaptation is considered to be the major factor in simultaneous color contrast [3.2.2a.].

3.8   Certain complex psychological factors can affect color responses.

3.8.1   Under everyday conditions, most object-color perceptions are largely independent of changes in illumination and viewing conditions; this phenomenon is called *color constancy.*

a. In the observations of everyday life, color constancy is usually complete in the sense that ordinary changes in illuminating and viewing conditions do not result in any disturbing changes in object-color perceptions.

1. In general, a familiar object continues to arouse approximately the same color perception whether viewed in average daylight or in incandescent lamplight, even though the energy characteristics of the light from the object are quite different under the two conditions.

2. Color constancy is considered to represent a complex *compensation* for changes in illumination or viewing conditions.

[3.8.1]

b. Color constancy can be enhanced or reduced by variations in stimulus factors, viewing conditions, and observer's attitude (68, 86, 88, 129, 164, 178, 278).

1. Color constancy is usually confined to the surface and volume modes of color perception [2.3.2e.].

2. Color constancy is favored by a low degree of selectivity in the illumination.

3. Color constancy is ordinarily reduced by very rapid or very great changes in the intensity or wavelength distribution of the illumination.

4. Color constancy is favored by relatively high reflectance in the surroundings of the stimulus object; color constancy is essentially lacking for a stimulus-object on a dark background.

5. Color constancy is aided by familiarity of objects, because of associated stable memory colors that help maintain a constant appearance; what is seen may be influenced more by what is remembered than by the spectral characteristics of the stimulus.

6. Color constancy is ordinarily enhanced by all factors that tend to heighten the *object* character of the perception.

a) The figures in highly organized figure-ground perceptions are especially subject to color constancy.

b) The visual resolution of fine microstructure is a favorable condition for color constancy.

1) For visually simple objects, a lack of resolution of surface structure may permit a shift from surface to film mode of appearance in which all constancy is lost.

c) The authenticity of objects in original scenes makes such scenes more favorable for color constancy than pictures of the scenes.

7. Color constancy requires awareness of the illumination as separate from the object.

a) A complex visual field is favorable for color constancy because of the numerous clues afforded by shaded and unshaded areas.

[3.8.1b.]

8. Color constancy can be very greatly affected by the *attitude* of the observer.

a) An *object-directed attitude* favors color constancy; this involves recognition of an object as such and the remembered color associated with it [3.8.3e.].

b) An *analytic attitude* disfavors color constancy; careful observation permits the spectral characteristics of the stimulus to play a major part in the perception [3.8.3f.].

c) Many persons can voluntarily change their observational attitude to such an extent that striking changes in color constancy can be produced.

d) There are large and persistent individual differences in color constancy, probably caused by differences in training and hence in attitude when observing.

c. Numerous measurements of the degree of color constancy have been made in experimental situations (33, 179, 204, 267).

1. Measurements of color constancy show that under experimental conditions a high degree of constancy is often found but a limited degree is not unusual.

a) Because of the limited degree of constancy typical of many experimental measurements, expressions like *partial color constancy* or *approximate color constancy* have been suggested as more appropriate labels for the phenomenon as observed under such conditions.

2. Most experimental work on color constancy has been limited to studies of *lightness constancy* or *approximate lightness constancy*.

3. Degree of color constancy found in any given experimental situation may be expressed as a *Brunswik ratio*.

a) A Brunswik ratio shows to what degree a stimulus-object retains the same object-color when viewing conditions are changed.

b) The Brunswik ratio has typically been used in experiments designed to show how constant the lightness of the response to a stimulus-object remains when the object is placed in shadow.

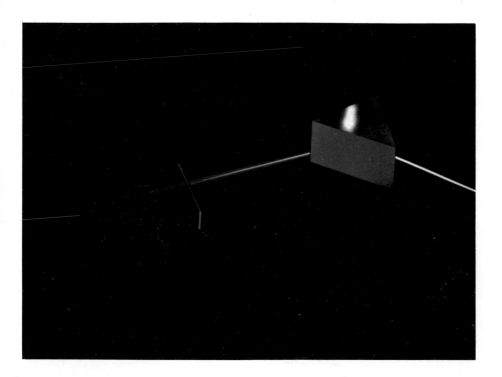

Fig. 2-8 Absorption of light by an optical filter. Light is dispersed by a prism and directed onto a "red" filter. The filter absorbs all but the long wavelength energy which passes through it.

Fig. 3-5 Effect of area on saturation and brightness. Up to a certain angular size, as an area becomes larger the brightness and saturation associated with it increase. The two areas shown here were printed with identical inks; the only physical difference between them lies in their sizes.

Fig. 3-6   Effect of contrast on brightness. The same gray ring appears either dark or light depending upon whether it is surrounded by a light or a dark area.

Fig. 3-7 Effect of contrast on saturation. The two rings have been printed with the same ink; the differences observed in their relative saturations result from the difference in contrast with their backgrounds.

Fig. 3-8   Effect of contrast with different hues on saturation. The two rings have been printed with the same ink. The different surround areas cause them to produce different saturations.

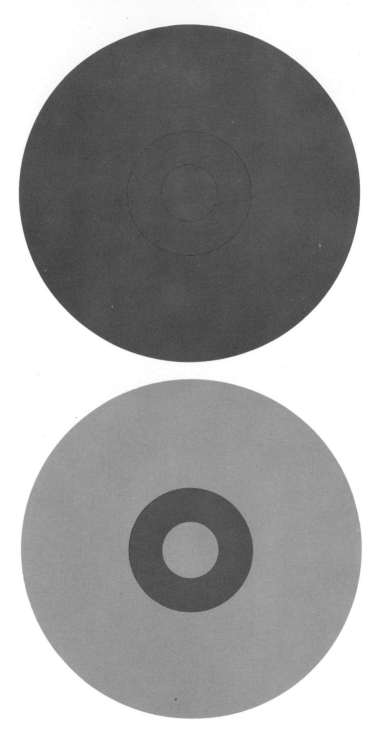

Fig. 3-9   Effect of contrast on hue. The two rings have been printed with the same ink. They produce different hues because of contrast with their surrounds.

Fig. 3-10   Effect of sharpness of contour on saturation and brightness. The two circles have been printed with the same ink. They differ only in the sharpness with which their edges are delineated.

Fig. 3-11 Effect of sharpness of contour on saturation and brightness. The two pictures are physically identical except for the degree of sharpness in their reproduction. Many differences may be seen in their appearances. In general, the sharper picture exhibits darker areas of higher saturation. The overall contrast of the sharp image appears to be higher than that of the unsharp image.

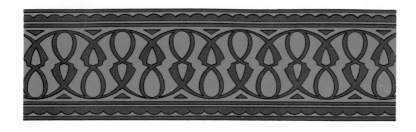

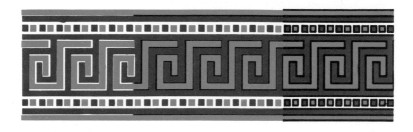

Fig. 3-12   Von Bezold spreading effect. The appearance of any area of red or blue depends largely on the colors of the adjacent areas. The appearance shifts are opposite to those that would be predicted on the basis of contrast. The phenomenon is referred to as spreading or assimilation. (*From:* Evans, R. M., *An Introduction to Color,* New York, John Wiley & Sons, Inc., 1948, Plate XI.)

Fig. 3-17 Demonstration of complementary afterimage. Stare at the white dot in the center of the chromatic areas for about a minute. Then look at the black dot in the bottom half of the figure. A complementary afterimage should appear.

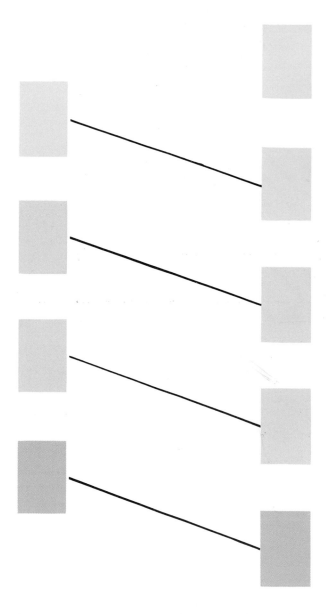

Fig. 3-21 End effect on series of samples for which saturation is seen to vary. The two rows of chromatic patches have been printed in such a way as to produce equal increments in saturation. The first four patches in each row comprise physically identical pairs. The fourth patch in the first row produces higher saturation than the fourth patch in the second row because the former is not followed by other patches.

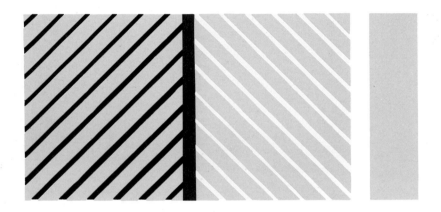

Fig. 3-23 The gray background is physically constant throughout
the illustration. It appears yellowish when interlaced with yellow
lines and bluish when interlaced with blue lines because of assimilation.

Fig. 3-24 Figure-ground effect. The appearance of an area may depend to a significant extent upon attitude. If the center of the Maltese cross is assumed to be related to the blue cross, it appears to be a bluish gray. If it is assumed to be the center of the yellow cross, however, it appears as a yellowish gray. Similarly, the black circular sectors serve to imply the presence of a white triangle. The implied triangle appears to be brighter than the surrounding white background, even though the continuous background is physically identical at all places.

Fig. 4-1   Appearance of chromatic samples to normal and color-deficient observers. The approximate appearance of a chromatic scene (as perceived by a normal observer in the upper left) is shown for a severe protan (upper right), severe deutan (lower left), and severe tritan (lower right).

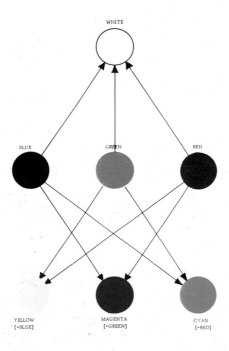

Fig. 5-1 Schematic diagram of additive color-stimulus synthesis. The red, green, and blue primaries may be combined additively to form combinations for which the end-point is white.

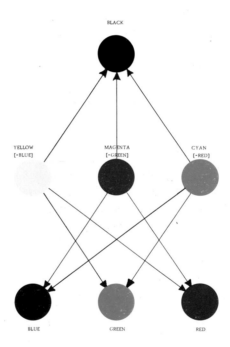

Fig. 5-2   Schematic diagram of subtractive color-stimulus synthesis. The cyan, magenta, and yellow primaries may be combined subtractively to form combinations for which the end-point is black.

[3.8.1c.3.]

c) The Brunswik ratio for the expression of lightness is

$$\frac{S - S'}{L - S'}$$

where L = measured luminance of the unshadowed object.
S' = measured luminance of the shadowed object.
S = luminance of the experimental match to the shadowed object.

1) The *Thouless ratio,* utilizing log luminances, has been suggested as an alternative to the Brunswik ratio as a means of better approximating sensory magnitude.

d) The Brunswik ratio may be adapted to experiments dealing with changes in quality as well as level of illumination and extended to all three dimensions of color.

1) Munsell units of hue, value, and chroma may be used separately in Brunswik ratios to give measures respectively of hue, lightness, and saturation constancy (203).
2) Munsell units of hue, value, and chroma may be inserted in formulas like the Godlove small-color-difference formula to compute differences that may then be inserted in a Brunswik ratio to give a measure of overall color constancy [7.5.2b.] (203).

4. Under experimental conditions the measured ratios for color constancy have been found to vary from zero to one (or occasionally over one) depending upon observers and viewing conditions.

3.8.2 The arrangement and meaningfulness of object patterns, e.g., *figure-ground relationships,* can affect the colors that are perceived.

a. The simple spatial ordering of a set of stimulus-objects can affect the colors that are perceived.

1. When a series of chromatic samples of the same dominant wavelength and luminance is arranged on a neutral ground in order of purity, the purest, or end sample, is likely to appear more saturated than it would if followed by still purer samples; this phenomenon is known as the *end effect* [Fig. 3.21].

[3.8.2]

b. Very simple changes in borders and boundary lines can result in striking changes in color perceptions.

1. If two crosses are cut from the same strip of gray paper and placed on white and black backgrounds respectively, a marked brightness difference between the responses to the crosses can be noted until the crosses are connected by a strip of the same gray, at which time the responses to them tend to become identical in brightness; this phenomenon has been called *color assimilation* [Fig. 3.22] (84). [3.2.2b. for a second use of this term and Fig. 3.23 for an illustration of this usage.]

3.8.3 Change in the intent or *mental set* of the observer is a major factor in determining what color is perceived.

a. A given visual phenomenon may not be perceived at all unless it is actively looked for.

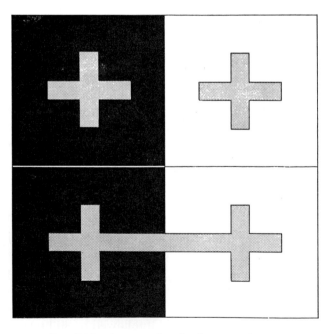

Fig. 3.22   An example of color assimilation.

[3.8.3]

b. Skepticism or negative suggestion concerning a visual phenomenon can prevent its occurrence.

c. When an object is perceived as belonging to one part of a figure or ground, the color response to the object may be somewhat different from that which is aroused when the object is perceived as belonging to a different part of the figure or ground [Fig. 3.24].

d. *Individual differences* and individual variability in perception are especially dependent upon the factor of set.

e. A *synthetic* or *object-directed attitude* is one that normally leads to the natural and naive type of perceptual response which people usually make in recognizing objects and is the attitude that results in impressions characteristic of remembered properties of the object.

f. An *analytic* or *subjective attitude* is one in which the observer is not so much concerned with remembered properties of the object as he is with interpreting the actual physical stimulation coming to him from that direction.

3.8.4   The memory that an observer has concerning the color associated with a particular object can influence the color that is perceived.

a. *Memory color* has been defined as the color perception that, according to the judgment of the observer, a familiar object would arouse if that object were under the illumination in which it is customarily seen.

b. Memory colors tend to accent dominant color characteristics.

1. On the basis of memory color it has been found that an observer typically selects a color which is too bright to match a bright memory-object, too dark to match a dark memory-object, and too saturated to match an object known to arouse distinct hue (165).

2. Memory colors for familiar objects show distinct hue shifts as well as changes in the other color dimensions (12, 202).

c. There is some indication that, in painting and photography, the greatest satisfaction to the observer is likely to result if the memory colors corresponding to familiar objects are matched rather than the actual colors aroused by the original subject (11).

[3.8.4c.]

1. For common natural things like human skin, sky, sand, grass, etc., memory colors of many observers are quite consistent and seem most representative of the original scene and most pleasing (12, 202).

3.9 Controlled observations of the very complex nature of everyday color perceptions have led to the formulation of a comprehensive principle, called *adaptation level*, which refers to the *frame of reference* against which an individual evaluates the characteristics of all the stimuli that he perceives (124).

3.9.1 Adaptation-level theory assumes that colors arise because of adaptation as a phenomenon of level, of gradient from level, or as combinations of the two effects.

3.9.2 In every viewing situation an adaptation level is established such that objects having reflectances above that level arouse responses which tend to take on the hue produced by the illuminant, objects having reflectances below that level arouse responses that tend to take on the hue of the after-image complementary, and objects of low purity relative to the weighted mean chromaticity of the field and having reflectances about equal to that of the adaptation level tend to appear as neutral or achromatic. This has been called the *Helson-Judd effect* [Fig. 3.25].

3.9.3 According to the principle of adaptation level, contrast is regarded as the establishment of gradients not with respect to reflectances of adjacent surfaces but with respect to adaptation level, which tends to be lower than the average of the reflectances of the surfaces.

3.9.4 Adaptation-level theory implies that any stimulus, regardless of its physical composition, may, with suitable context, appear achromatic; all other stimuli will appear chromatic with respect to the neutral adaptation level according to their luminance, dominant wavelength, and purity *relations* to the luminance, dominant wavelength, and purity of the stimulus that appears neutral [Fig. 3.26].

a. A spatially complex mixture of the light from two sources of perceptibly different hue may, in the best situations, produce virtually all hues rather than merely the two hues normally produced by the illuminants and their simple mixtures.

[3.9.4]

b. With a spatially complex luminance mixture of the light from a source having a dominant wavelength of 550 mμ and one having a dominant wavelength of 600 mμ: (*a*) areas having a reflectance about equal to the adaptation level reflectance and about equal amounts of the light from each source will appear neutral; (*b*) areas having about equal amounts of the light from

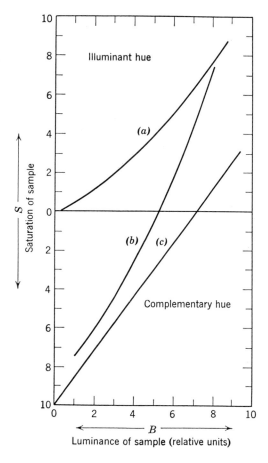

Fig. 3.25 Schematic representation of saturation and hue under highly chromatic illumination as a function of reflectance of the sample for (*a*) black background, (*b*) gray background, and (*c*) white background. From Evans, R. M., Hanson, W. T., Jr., and Brewer, W. L., *Principles of Color Photography*, New York: John Wiley & Sons, Inc., 1953, Fig. 3-15, p. 135.

[3.9.4b.]

each source, but reflectances higher or lower than the reflectance of the adaptation level, will tend to evoke the hue produced by the apparent illuminant mixture and the hue complementary to that produced by the apparent illuminant mixture, respectively; (*c*) the illuminants themselves will appear to have an exaggerated hue-difference (the 550 mμ illuminant will appear green and the 600 mμ illuminant will appear red); (*d*) the apparent illuminant mixture will appear yellow and its hue-complement will appear bluish, so that red, green, blue, and yellow hues plus their apparent mixtures will all be seen in addition to neutrals in an ideal situation, even though, under different adaptation

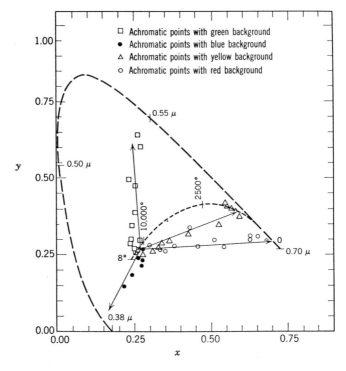

Fig. 3.26 Achromatic loci: The dashed curve shows the spectral locus, with wavelengths in microns; the dotted curve is the locus of black-body radiators, with temperatures in degrees Kelvin; the solid lines join the "white point" with the background points. From Helson, H. and Michels, W. C., *J. opt. Soc. Amer.*, 1948, *38*, Fig. 1, p. 1029.

[3.9.4]

conditions, the two illuminants might both appear green or yellowish green.

c. According to adaptation-level theory it is the *relativity* of stimuli that determine the colors aroused by them.

3.9.5 Notable demonstrations of heterochromatic images arising as a result of adaptation level in unusual stimulus situations have been made by R. M. Evans (66) and E. H. Land (172, 173).

3.10 Color vision varies to some extent as a function of the age of the observer.

3.10.1 There is evidence for selective hue-response in the infant within the first several weeks after birth (44, 253).

3.10.2 Rapid improvement has been reported for color discrimination up to about the age of 25 years, followed by a gradual decline which becomes more pronounced around age 65.

a. The ability to distinguish colors develops more rapidly than the ability to name them.

b. Children do not do as well as adults on pseudoisochromatic tests of color vision (42).

3.10.3 The decline in color ability can be accounted for, in part at least, by certain physiological and psychophysiological factors which decline with age.

a. The rate of just-perceptible flicker and the rate of dark adaptation both decline with age.

b. The size of the peripheral visual field contracts with increasing age.

c. Iris pigmentation changes with increasing age, and the transmittance of the ocular media falls off progressively.

d. As age increases, the lenses develop a melanin-type pigment like that in the skin.

1. Less of the incident energy (particularly short-wave energy) reaches the light-sensitive elements of the retina as the individual grows older.

2. Individuals become less sensitive to short-wavelength light as they grow older.

[3.10]

3.10.4 Compensatory psychological factors, such as intelligence and experience, can combat, more or less effectively, the decline of visual ability due to increasing age.

a. The more that proficiency in a special field depends upon accumulated experience, rather than sheer efficiency of the visual receptor, the longer does proficiency tend to improve.

Chapter Four

Defective Color Vision

Defective color vision, often called color blindness, refers to a variety of abnormal physiological conditions, usually congenital, which produce deviant color responses or fewer color responses than normal (49, 93, 158, 159, 292).

4.1 There are three main forms of abnormal color-vision systems: monochromatism (or achromatopsia), dichromatism, and anomalous trichromatism.

4.1.1 *Monochromatism, achromatopsia,* or *achromatopia* (also called *total color blindness*) is the abnormal color-vision system in which the afflicted individual makes only achromatic visual responses; two subtypes of monochromatism can be distinguished.

a. In *typical monochromatism,* there is apparently a complete or nearly complete lack of functioning of the retinal cone mechanism.

1. In typical monochromatism, the luminosity curve at photopic stimulus intensities resembles the normal scotopic luminosity curve, with a maximum at about 500 mμ.
2. In typical monochromatism, there is always reduced foveal acuity, accompanied usually by small central scotoma, nystagmoid eye movements, and photophobic symptoms.

b. In *atypical monochromatism,* there is apparently a defect in the higher nerve centers or in the conducting pathways of the visual system rather than in the retina.

[4.1.1b.]

1. In atypical monochromatism, the luminosity curve is usually nearly normal (with a maximum at about 560 mμ), there is no reduction in foveal acuity, and there are no nystagmoid eye movements or photophobic symptoms.

4.1.2 *Dichromatism* is the abnormal color-vision system in which the afflicted individual is capable of making only *two* kinds of color distinctions (light-dark and either yellow-blue or red-green), that is, all color stimuli can be matched with appropriate mixtures of only two stimulus primaries.   In general, all color stimuli that match for the normal (trichromatic) observer also match for the dichromat, but the reverse is not true.   The dichromat has many more metameric color stimuli than the normal trichromat [5.3 and 6.3.3c.1.a)2)].

a. Four types of dichromatism can be distinguished: protanopia, deuteranopia, tritanopia, and tetartanopia.

1. *Protanopia* (sometimes erroneously called "red blindness") is a type of dichromatism in which the afflicted individual confuses stimuli that are normally seen as red and bluish green with neutral and with each other (all three are seen as neutral) [Fig. 4.1].

a) The most distinctive feature of protanopia is a shortening of the long-wave end of the visible spectrum; the protanope makes neither chromatic nor achromatic responses to spectral stimuli beyond about 680 mμ.

b) The protanope sees only two hues (blue and yellow) in the spectrum, with an average neutral point at about 492 mμ for illuminant C.   The protanope has a second neutral point in the extra-spectral chromaticity region normally seen as a yellowish red [Fig. 4.2] [6.3.3c.1.b)5)].

1) The protanope sees light of all wavelengths as some saturation of blue or yellow, and saturation decreases to zero as the neutral points in the hue circle are approached.

c) The luminosity function of the protanope appears shifted toward the short-wave end of the spectrum, with a maximum at about 540 mμ [Fig. 4.3].

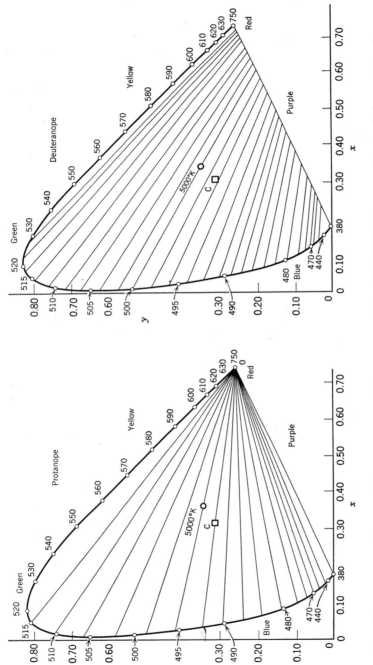

Fig. 4.2 Chromaticity confusions of the protanope and deuteranope (after Pitt, 1935) shown on the (x,y)-chromaticity diagram. The typical protanope, for example, will not be able to distinguish source C from a part of the spectrum near 493 mμ. From Stevens, S. S. (Ed.), *Handbook of Experimental Psychology*, New York: John Wiley & Sons, Inc., 1951, Fig. 12, p. 844 (solid lines only).

[4.1.2a.]

2. *Deuteranopia* (sometimes erroneously called "green blindness") is a type of dichromatism in which the afflicted individual confuses stimuli that are normally seen as bluish red and green with neutral and with each other (all three are seen as neutral) [Fig. 4.1].

a) The deuteranope sees only two hues (blue and yellow) in the spectrum, with an average neutral point at about 498 mμ for illuminant C. The deuteranope also sees neutral in the extra-spectral hue region normally seen as a bluish red [Fig. 4.2].

1) The deuteranope (like the protanope) sees light of all wavelengths as some saturation of blue or yellow, and

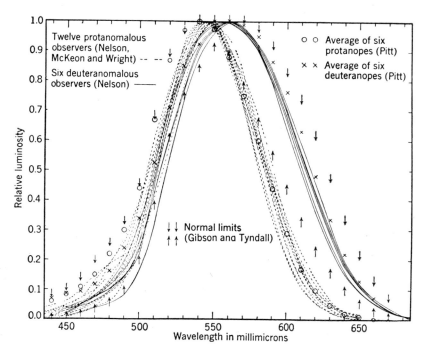

Fig. 4.3   Relative spectral luminosity for normal and color-deviant observers (after Judd, 1943). From Judd, D. B., *Color in Business, Science, and Industry,* New York: John Wiley & Sons, Inc., 1952, Fig. 20, p. 69.

[4.1.2a.2.]

saturation decreases to zero as the neutral points are approached in the hue circle.

b) The average location of the maximum of the luminosity curve for the deuteranope is about 560 mμ [Fig. 4.3].

c) Principal differences between the protanope and deuteranope are that their neutral points fall at different parts of the hue circle and that the long-wavelength end of the spectrum is comparatively darker for the protanope.

3. *Tritanopia* is a type of dichromatism in which the afflicted person confuses stimuli that are normally seen as purplish blue and greenish yellow with neutral and with each other (all three are seen as neutral) [Figs. 4.1 and 4.4].

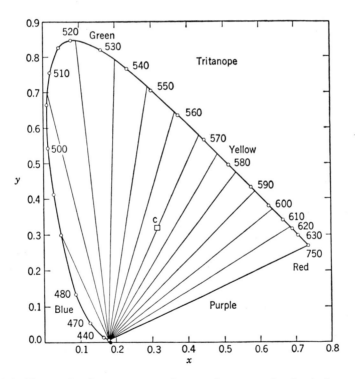

Fig. 4.4   Tritanopic chromaticity confusions shown on the (x,y)-chromaticity diagram.   From Judd, D. B., *Color in Business, Science, and Industry*, New York: John Wiley & Sons, Inc., 1952, Fig. 29c, p. 107.

[4.1.2a.3.]

a) The tritanope sees only two hues (red and green) in the spectrum, with a neutral point at about 570 mμ and sometimes a second neutral point at about 430 mμ and lower. **b)** The luminosity function for the tritanope is normal, or nearly so, with a maximum at about 560 mμ, but with a possible weakness at the short-wave end of the spectrum.

4. *Tetartanopia* is an exceedingly rare and less certainly established type of dichromatism to which certain cases of blue-yellow defect are sometimes assigned.

a) The tetartanope is said to have two neutral points in the spectrum, at about 580 and 470 mμ.

1) To the tetartanope the spectrum appears red at the long-wave end, green in the middle, and red again at the short-wave end.
2) No uncomplicated case of tetartanopia has ever been reported.

4.1.3 *Anomalous trichromatism* is the abnormal color-vision system that departs least severely from the normal trichromatic system; the anomalous trichromat requires three stimulus primaries to match all color stimuli, but his matches do not fall within the normal range of variation.

a. Three types of anomalous trichromatism can be distinguished: *protanomaly, deuteranomaly,* and *tritanomaly.*

1. The terms *protan, deutan,* and *tritan* have been suggested for describing individuals with various types of anomalous trichromatism (288). These terms are intended to apply to conditions of varying severity of anomaly, thus implying that the difference between dichromatism and anomalous trichromatism is theoretically one of degree rather than of kind.
2. The *protanomalous trichromats* (protans) are considered to be red weak because, in a red-green mixture (of stimuli that respectively yield red and green responses), they require more than a normal amount of red to match a given yellow.

a) The luminosity function for all degrees of protanomaly seems to be deficient at the long-wave end of the spectrum and has a maximum at about 540 mμ.

[4.1.3a.]

3. The *deuteranomalous trichromats* (deutans) are said to be green weak, because, in a red-green mixture, they require more than a normal amount of green to match a given yellow.

a) The deuteranomalous trichromat has a luminosity function well within the variations found in the luminosity functions of normals.

4. The *tritanomalous trichromats* (tritans) are considered to be blue weak because, in a blue-green mixture, they require more than a normal amount of blue to match a given blue-green.

b. Anomalous trichromats can make, with more or less difficulty, the color distinctions that the corresponding dichromat cannot make at all.

1. With large stimuli under favorable conditions of lighting, adaptation, and brief viewing time, anomalous trichromats seem to see much the same colors as the normal, but ordinarily they differ significantly from the normal in the mixtures they require for color matches.

4.2 Defective color vision can be due to an inherited characteristic transmitted as a sex-linked characteristic [Fig. 4.5].

4.2.1 If a female has normal color vision she may have either one or no defective genes for color vision.

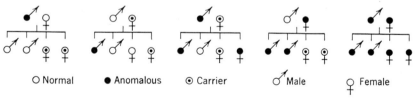

O Normal   ● Anomalous   ⊙ Carrier   ♂ Male   ♀ Female

Inheritance of anomalous color vision

Fig. 4.5 Inheritance of anomalous color vision. (O normal, ● anomalous, ⊙ carrier, ♂ male, ♀ female). From LeGrand, Yves, *Light, Colour, and Vision*, p. 335. (Translated by R. W. G. Hunt, J. W. T. Walsh, and F. R. W. Hunt, New York: John Wiley & Sons, Inc., 1957.)

[4.2.1]

a. If a female has one defective gene for color vision, half her sons (on the average) will have defective color vision.

b. If a female has one defective gene for color vision and her mate is color-normal, half their daughters (on the average) will have one defective gene, but none will have defective color vision.

c. If a female has one defective gene for color vision and her mate has defective color vision, half their sons and half their daughters will have defective color vision and half their daughters will have one defective gene (on the average).

d. If a female has no defective genes for color vision and her mate has defective color vision, all their children will have normal color vision but all their daughters will have one defective gene for color vision.

4.2.2   If a female has congenital defective color vision, both her genes for color vision will be defective.

a. If a female has congenital defective color vision and her mate has normal color vision, all their sons will have defective color vision and all their daughters will have one defective gene for color vision.

b. If both a female and her mate have congenital defective color vision, all their children will have defective color vision.

4.3   Color-vision defects can be caused by a disease or toxic agent which affects the retina, optic nerve, or optic cortex; in such cases the color vision defects are called *acquired color defects* or *acquired color blindness*.

4.3.1   The most common disease that causes central color defects is multiple sclerosis.

4.3.2   Optic neuritis with loss of color and form discrimination is caused most commonly by blood dyscrasias such as pernicious anemia, secondary anemia, or leukemia, and by deficiency diseases such as vitamin B_1 deficiency, so-called "diabetic amblyopia," and optic neuritis of pregnancy.

4.3.3   The most common occurrences of a defect of color perception in the center of the retina are in connection with toxic amblyopia and the poisons that most commonly cause such loss of

[4.3]

sensitivity are: carbon disulfide, lead poisoning, spinal anesthesia, sulfanilamide, snuff, iodoform, stramonium, thallium, tobacco, and alcohol.

4.3.4 Toxic agents and disease affecting the conducting parts of the visual mechanism (nerve fiber layer of the retina, optic nerve, and tract) are supposed to cause *acquired red-green weakness.*

> **a.** Acquired red-green weakness is accompanied by less than normal visual acuity and the ability to distinguish only yellow from blue and light from dark.
>
> **b.** Acquired red-green weakness becomes progressively worse until the deuteranopic form of red-green defect results and is often called *progressive red-green blindness.*
>
> **c.** If poisoning or disease continues, acquired red-green weakness can result in monochromatism.

4.3.5 Injuries to the rod-cone mechanism result first in a depression of sensitivity to yellow-blue discriminations, called *acquired tritanopia.*

> **a.** Acquired tritanopia may become stabilized and is often localized in a small area of the retina.
>
> **b.** Acquired tritanopia leads to monochromatism only when progressive red-green blindness follows.

4.3.6 Sometimes the damage done in acquired color defects is slight and temporary; in other cases it is permanent.

4.4 The incidence of color-vision defects in the general population varies widely with the type of defect [Table 4.1].

4.4.1 The incidence of color-vision defects found in several studies among school children was about 8 percent for boys and less than ½ percent for girls (222, 275).

> **a.** Protanomaly was found in 1.0 percent of males and 0.02 percent of females.
>
> **b.** Deuteranomaly was found in about 4.9 percent of males and 0.38 percent of females.
>
> **c.** Protanopia was found in about 1.0 percent of males and 0.02 percent of females.

[4.4.1]

d. Deuteranopia was found in about 1.1 percent of males and 0.01 percent of females.
e. Tritanopia was found in about 0.0001 percent of males and none of the females.
f. Congenital monochromatism was found in about 0.003 percent of males and 0.002 percent of females.

Table 4.1   Incidence of Anomalous Color Vision

Authority	Subjects	Males	Females	Total
1. C. Bally	1000 10-year-old boys	9%	—	—
2. C. Burt	English school children	—	—	6%
3. E. Chan and W. S. Mae	Unselected group	4.97%	0.71%	5.68%
4. F. Clements	624 American Indians	—	—	1.92%
5. F. Clements	American Negro group	—	—	3.71%
6. F. Clements	Todas in Southern India	—	—	12.8%
7. K. Crooks	Negro group	3.75%	0%	3.75%
8. G. DeWaele	600 unselected subjects	—	—	9.0%
9. T. R. Garth	Turkish subjects	5.3%	0%	5.3%
10. W. R. Geddes	Fijian natives	—	—	0.5%
11. J. Hiernaux and H. van der Borght	Negroid races	—	—	1.8–4%
12. J. Hiernaux and H. van der Borght	Caucasian race	—	—	8%
13. H. H. Hsiae	Chinese school children	5.57%	0.58%	6.15%
14. L. G. Kilborn and Y. T. Beh	2279 Chinese males 1132 Chinese females	6.5%	1.7%	8.2%
15. F. R. Neubert	40,380 subjects	—	—	5.5%
16. N. O'Conner	Imbeciles	13%	—	—
17. P. von Planta	2000 unselected males 2000 unselected females	7.98%	0.43%	8.41%
18. J. Scully	English school children	4.9%	0.4%	5.3%
19. K. Simon	Baganda Africans	—	—	1.86%
20. P. E. Vernon and A. Straker	English males	7.49%	—	—
21. G. M. H. Waaler	9000 Norwegian school children	8.01%	0.44%	8.45%

J. Cloak and L. C. Becker, "Bibliography on Color Blindness," University of Wisconsin Communications Research Project No. 1, 1960.

[4.4]

4.4.2 The incidence of color-vision defects apparently varies widely with various ethnic and regional groups (168).

a. Very low rates of incidence of color vision defects in males have been found, for example, among Fijis (0.8%), Navajo Indians (1.1%), and Belgian Congo Negroes (1.7%), while high rates of incidence in males have been found among Canadians (11.2%), Poles (10.7%), Czechoslovakians (10.5%), and Norwegians (10.1%).

4.4.3 There are reported to be more than 10 million people with a red-green defect in the United States.

Section II

Applied Facts

Chapter Five

Facts Basic to Color-Stimulus

Measurement

The basis for color-stimulus specification lies in the process of determining the physical stimuli (typically in an isolated field) that produce identical responses of hue, saturation, and brightness, and the process is called color matching (49, 67, 93, 159, 292, 293).

5.1   The process of determining the physical stimuli that produce the same brightness, regardless of hue and saturation, is called *brightness matching* and is the basis for photometry.   Brightness matching is merely a limited case of *color matching*.

5.1.1   Any determination of stimuli that produce the same brightness is restricted to the conditions under which the match was obtained.

a. A brightness match produced by color stimuli at a given visual angle [3.2.1a.] may not hold for the same stimuli when they subtend a significantly different visual angle.
b. A brightness match produced by stimuli in a given visual field may not hold in another field.
c. A brightness match produced by stimuli that excite one part of the retina may not hold when the same stimuli are directed to other parts of the retina.

[5.1.1]

d. The color stimuli that produce a brightness match under one condition of adaptation may not produce a match under another adaptation, although the match may hold over a large range of adaptation conditions [3.7].

5.1.2 Brightness matching is usually restricted to foveal areas of the retina at adaptation levels high enough to be considered photopic [2.2.3c. and 3.1.2c.4.a)].

a. Brightness matching may be performed when two stimuli excite adjacent parts of the retina at the same time; this is called *direct matching.*

b. Brightness matching may be performed when two stimuli alternately excite the same portion of the retina; this is called the *flicker method of brightness matching.* This method is used in *flicker photometry.*

5.1.3 Whenever two color stimuli are compared and the intensity of one stimulus can be adjusted to produce a color match, this adjustment of intensity is called *homochromatic brightness matching.*

a. Homochromatic brightness matching by no means implies the limited use of single-frequency stimuli comprising identical, narrow spectral bands; it refers to brightness matching that produces a hue and saturation match also.

b. When the intensities of otherwise identical stimuli are adjusted so that they produce the same brightness, the two stimuli will essentially be physically identical and must therefore produce colors that match in hue and saturation as well.

c. Homochromatic brightness matching is relatively easy to perform, even for inexperienced observers, because a brightness match will result in identical colors for the two stimuli.

5.1.4 Whenever the responses to two stimuli of dissimilar dominant wavelength and purity are compared, it is sometimes difficult, but nevertheless possible, to determine whether or not they produce equal brightnesses. If the intensity of one of the stimuli can be varied, it is possible to equate them for brightness. This procedure is called *heterochromatic brightness matching* or *heterochromatic photometry.*

[5.1.4]

a. Heterochromatic brightness matching may be performed either by *direct matching* or by the *flicker method.*

1. The direct method of heterochromatic brightness matching is typically used when it is desired to compare the responses of stimuli of nearly the same wavelength composition, because differences in hue and saturation are minimized.
2. The flicker method of heterochromatic brightness matching involves the alternate presentation of stimuli at a frequency above that at which chromaticness differences in the responses to the two stimuli are apparent and only that flicker associated with brightness differences persists. When the flicker due to brightness differences is minimized or eliminated by adjusting the intensity of one or both alternating stimuli, the two components are sometimes considered to have the same brightness.

5.1.5 Stimulus intensities may be related to visual response in terms of *luminous flux* [5.1.6c.].

a. The *luminosity function* represents the reciprocal of the radiant flux required for single-frequency stimuli, throughout the spectrum, to produce a brightness match for some fixed stimulus [3.1.2c.].
b. The *Commission Internationale d'Éclairage* (CIE) in 1924 adopted a standard relative luminosity function for photopic vision [Fig. 3.4] (142).

1. The *standard observer* represented by the CIE photopic luminosity function was derived from the average of the results of several heterochromatic brightness-matching experiments.
2. The wavelength of maximum luminosity (the wavelength at which the relative luminosity coefficient is set equal to unity) for the CIE photopic luminosity function is 555 mμ.

c. The CIE in 1951 adopted a standard luminosity function for *scotopic* vision [Fig. 3.4] (10).

1. The standard observer represented by the CIE scotopic luminosity function is based on the results of homochromatic

[5.1.5c.1.]

brightness matching of dark-adapted observers whose ages did not exceed 30 years.

a) Brightness matching at scotopic (low) levels of illumination is always homochromatic, regardless of wavelength, because only rod vision is operating.

2. The wavelength of maximum luminosity for the CIE scotopic luminosity function is 507 mμ.

5.1.6 Two general conventions have been adopted to provide a basis for deriving *photometric units*.

a. The CIE 1924 standard luminosity function for photopic vision is the first of two conventions that serve as a basis for deriving photometric units.

b. The assumption that the total luminous flux, i.e., the rate of transfer of visually effective radiant energy, is given by the arithmetical sum of the individual luminous flux contributions of the spectral components in a beam of light is the second of two conventions that serve as a basis for deriving photometric units.

c. The two conventions that have been adopted as a basis for deriving photometric units are implicit in the definition of *luminous flux* (F) as given by the equation:

$$F = K(m) \int P(\lambda) \cdot V(\lambda) \cdot d\lambda$$

where $P(\lambda)$ = the radiant flux in watts between the wavelength limits λ and $\lambda + d\lambda$,

$V(\lambda)$ = the relative luminous (visual) efficiency at wavelength λ,

$K(m)$ = the luminous efficiency in lumens per watt of the radiation $\lambda = 555$ mμ, for which $V(\lambda)$ is maximum.

d. The unit of luminous flux is the *lumen,* which serves as a basis for deriving photometric units of *luminance* and *illuminance.*

1. *Luminance* refers to the luminous flux radiated in a given direction per unit area perpendicular to this direction per unit solid angle (steradian) from a spatially extended source (in-

cluding secondary sources such as reflecting or transmitting objects). Luminance was formerly called *photometric brightness.*

a) Many units have been used to express luminance, but they are all simply related by combinations of π and appropriate coefficients needed to express the relation between various measures of surface area [Table 5.1].

2. *Illuminance* refers to the areal density of the incident luminous flux, i.e., flux incident per unit area of a surface. Illuminance is sometimes called *illumination.*

a) A number of units have been used to express illuminance, but they are all simply related by coefficients needed to express the relation between various measures of surface area [Table 5.2].

3. The lumen is, by convention, equal to the flux emitted in a unit solid angle by a uniform point source of 1 candle; the total flux emitted by a uniform point source of 1 candle is 4π lumens.

a) A precise numerical relation exists between certain units of luminance and illuminance for the ideal perfectly diffusing, perfectly reflecting surface, which is called the *perfect diffuser.*

1) Since 1 foot-candle equals 1 lumen per square foot, a perfect diffuser subjected to an illumination of 1 foot-candle will have a luminance, regardless of the angle of view, of 1 foot-lambert.
2) The foot-lambert is sometimes referred to as the apparent or equivalent foot-candle.

e. The photometric unit of *retinal illuminance* is the *troland,* defined as equal to the luminance of 1 candle per square meter when the apparent area of the entrance pupil of the eye is 1 square millimeter.

1. The troland was at one time called the photon. In order to eliminate confusion with the elementary quantum of light

[5.1.6e.]

(photon), the unit has been renamed after its originator, L. T. Troland.

2. The amount of retinal illuminance for a normally incident stimulus through a small-diameter pupil is the product of stimulus luminance and the area of the pupil.

3. Light entering the pupil of the eye near its edge is less

Table 5.1 Luminance Units

Candle/cm² (Stilb)	1 —	3.183×10^{-1} $1/\pi$	1.550×10^{-1} $1/A$	1.076×10^{-3} $1/D$	3.426×10^{-4} $1/\pi D$
Lambert (Lumens/cm²)	3.1416 π	1 —	4.869×10^{-1} π/A	3.382×10^{-3} π/D	1.076×10^{-3} $1/D$
Candle/in.²	6.452 A	2.054 A/π	1 —	6.944×10^{-3} $1/C$	2.210×10^{-3} $1/\pi C$
Candle/ft²	9.290×10^{2} D	2.957×10^{2} D/π	1.44×10^{2} C	1 —	3.183×10^{-1} $1/\pi$
Foot-Lambert (apparent or equivalent ft candles) (Lumens/ft²)	2.919×10^{3} πD	9.290×10^{2} D	4.524×10^{2} πC	3.1416 π	1 —
Milli-Lambert	3.1416×10^{3} $\pi \times 10^{3}$	10^{3} —	4.869×10^{2} $\pi/A \times 10^{3}$	3.382 $\pi/D \times 10^{3}$	1.076 $1/D \times 10^{3}$
Candle/meter² (Nit, Blondel)	10^{4} F	3.183×10^{3} F/π	1.550×10^{3} E	1.076×10^{1} B	3.426 B/π
Lumen/meter² Apostilb (Asb) (Meter-Lambert)	3.1416×10^{4} πF	10^{4} F	4.869×10^{3} πE	3.382×10^{1} πB	1.076×10^{1} B
Milli-Foot-Lambert (app. or eq. Milli-Footcandles)	2.919×10^{6} $\pi D \times 10^{3}$	9.290×10^{5} $D \times 10^{3}$	4.524×10^{5} $\pi C \times 10^{3}$	3.1416×10^{3} $\pi \times 10^{3}$	10^{3} —
Micro-Lambert	3.1416×10^{6} $\pi \times 10^{6}$	10^{6} —	4.869×10^{5} $\pi/A \times 10^{6}$	3.382×10^{3} $\pi/D \times 10^{6}$	1.076×10^{3} $1/D \times 10^{6}$
Micro-Foot-Lambert (app. or eq. Micro-Footcandles)	2.919×10^{9} $\pi D \times 10^{6}$	9.290×10^{8} $D \times 10^{6}$	4.524×10^{8} $\pi C \times 10^{6}$	3.1416×10^{6} $\pi \times 10^{6}$	10^{6} —
Micro-Millilambert	3.1416×10^{9} $\pi \times 10^{9}$	10^{9} —	4.869×10^{8} $\pi/A \times 10^{9}$	3.382×10^{6} $\pi/D \times 10^{9}$	1.076×10^{6} $1/D \times 10^{9}$
Micro-Microlambert	3.1416×10^{12} $\pi \times 10^{12}$	10^{12} —	4.869×10^{11} $\pi/A \times 10^{12}$	3.382×10^{9} $\pi/D \times 10^{12}$	1.076×10^{9} $1/D \times 10^{12}$

Notation for Symbolic Values of Luminance Units: $\pi = 3.1416$, $A = 6.452 = $ (cm/in.)², $B = 10.76 = $ (ft/meter)², $C = 144 = $ (in./ft)², $D = 929.0 = $ (cm/ft)², $E = 1550 = $ (in./meter)², $F = 10^{4} = $ (cm/meter)².

To convert from one unit to another, read up or down from the diagonal. Example: 1 Millilambert $= 0.2957$ Candles/ft². (Data compiled by Mr. K. S. Weaver.)

[5.1.6e.]

effective in producing brightness than light entering the center of the pupil. This phenomenon is called the *Stiles-Crawford effect,* and because of it, the effective area of the pupil is smaller than the actual area.

4. Because of the Stiles-Crawford effect, the *effective troland,* which is the product of luminance and effective pupil area, is

3.183×10^{-4} $1/\pi \times 10^{-3}$	10^{-4} $1/F$	3.183×10^{-5} $1/\pi\,F$	3.426×10^{-7} $1/\pi D \times 10^{-3}$	3.183×10^{-7} $1/\pi \times 10^{-6}$	3.426×10^{-10} $1/\pi D \times 10^{-6}$	3.183×10^{-10} $1/\pi \times 10^{-3}$	3.183×10^{-13} $1/\pi \times 10^{-12}$
10^{-3} —	3.1416×10^{-4} π/F	10^{-4} $1/F$	1.076×10^{-6} $1/D \times 10^{-3}$	10^{-6} —	1.076×10^{-9} $1/D \times 10^{-6}$	10^{-9} —	10^{-12} —
2.054×10^{-3} $A/\pi \times 10^{-3}$	6.452×10^{-4} $1/E$	2.054×10^{-4} $1/E\,\pi$	2.210×10^{-6} $1/\pi C \times 10^{-3}$	2.054×10^{-6} $A/\pi \times 10^{-6}$	2.210×10^{-9} $1/\pi C \times 10^{-6}$	2.054×10^{-9} $A/\pi \times 10^{-9}$	2.054×10^{-12} $A/\pi \times 10^{-12}$
2.957×10^{-1} $D/\pi \times 10^{-3}$	9.290×10^{-2} $1/B$	2.957×10^{-2} $1/B\,\pi$	3.183×10^{-4} $1/\pi \times 10^{-3}$	2.957×10^{-4} $D/\pi \times 10^{-6}$	3.182×10^{-7} $1/\pi \times 10^{-6}$	2.957×10^{-7} $D/\pi \times 10^{-9}$	2.957×10^{-10} $D/\pi \times 10^{-9}$
9.290×10^{-1} $D \times 10^{-3}$	2.919×10^{-1} π/B	9.290×10^{-2} $1/B$	10^{-3} —	9.290×10^{-4} $D \times 10^{-6}$	10^{-6} —	9.290×10^{-7} $D \times 10^{-9}$	9.290×10^{-10} $D \times 10^{-12}$
1 —	3.1416×10^{-1} $\pi/F \times 10^3$	10^{-1} $1/F \times 10^3$	1.076×10^{-3} $1/D$	10^{-3} —	1.076×10^{-6} $1/D \times 10^{-3}$	10^{-6} —	10^{-9} —
3.183 $F/\pi \times 10^{-3}$	1 —	3.183×10^{-1} $1/\pi$	3.426×10^{-3} $B/\pi \times 10^{-3}$	3.183×10^{-3} $F/\pi \times 10^{-6}$	3.426×10^{-6} $B/\pi \times 10^{-6}$	3.183×10^{-6} $F/\pi \times 10^{-9}$	3.183×10^{-9} $F/\pi \times 10^{-12}$
10 $F \times 10^{-3}$	3.1416 π	1 —	1.076×10^{-2} $B \times 10^{-3}$	10^{-2} $F \times 10^{-6}$	1.076×10^{-5} $B \times 10^{-6}$	10^{-5} $F \times 10^{-9}$	10^{-8} $F \times 10^{-12}$
9.290×10^2 D	2.919×10^2 $\pi/B \times 10^3$	9.290×10^1 $1/B \times 10^3$	1 —	9.290×10^{-1} $D \times 10^{-3}$	10^{-3} —	9.290×10^{-4} $D \times 10^{-6}$	9.290×10^{-7} $D \times 10^{-9}$
10^3 —	3.1416×10^2 $\pi/F \times 10^6$	10^2 $1/F \times 10^6$	1.076 $1/D \times 10^3$	1 —	1.076×10^{-3} $1/D$	10^{-3} —	10^{-6} —
9.290×10^5 $D \times 10^3$	2.919×10^5 $\pi/B \times 10^6$	9.290×10^4 $1/B \times 10^6$	10^3 —	9.290×10^2 D	1 —	9.290×10^{-1} $D \times 10^{-3}$	9.290×10^{-4} $D \times 10^{-6}$
10^6 —	3.1416×10^5 $\pi/F \times 10^9$	10^5 $1/F \times 10^9$	1.076×10^{-3} $1/D \times 10^6$	10^3 —	1.076 $1/D \times 10^3$	1 —	10^{-3} —
10^9 —	3.1416×10^8 $\pi/F \times 10^{12}$	10^8 $1/F \times 10^{12}$	1.076×10^{-6} $1/D \times 10^9$	10^6 —	1.076×10^3 $1/D \times 10^6$	10^3 —	1 —

[5.1]

frequently used to specify the level of retinal illumination (93, p. 84).

5.2 The process of determining the physical stimuli that produce equality of hue, saturation, and brightness is called *color matching* and is the basis for *colorimetry*, defined as the technique of measuring and specifying color-stimuli.

5.2.1 Any determination of the equality of color produced by various stimuli is restricted to the conditions under which the match was obtained, except where it has been demonstrated that different conditions do not change the match significantly.

a. A color match, produced by color stimuli at a given visual angle, may not hold for the same stimuli when they subtend a different visual angle.

b. A color match, produced by stimuli in a given visual field, may not hold in another field.

c. A color match, produced by stimuli that excite one part of the retina, may not hold when the same stimuli are directed to other parts of the retina.

d. Juxtaposed stimuli that produce a color match under one state of adaptation will also provide a match under a wide range of other adaptation conditions.

1. From one adaptation to another the *color* associated with two juxtaposed matching areas will change, but usually the match will still hold.

Table 5.2   Illuminance Units

Phot	1	1.076×10^{-3}	10^{-3}	10^{-4}	10^{-6}
Foot-candle	9.29×10^2	1	9.29×10^{-1}	9.29×10^{-2}	9.29×10^{-4}
Milliphot	10^3	1.076	1	10^{-1}	10^{-3}
Meter-candle (Lux)	10^4	1.076×10	10	1	10^{-2}
Microphot	10^6	1.076×10^3	10^3	10^2	1

To convert from one unit to another, read up or down from the diagonal. Example: 1 foot-candle = 10.76 meter-candles. (Data compiled by Mr. K. S. Weaver.)

[5.2.1d.]

2. Two areas that produce a match in color under a variety of adaptation conditions may not continue to do so under extreme conditions, e.g., as either extreme of the photopic range is approached.

5.2.2 *Color mixture* is a traditional term that has been used to refer to the synthesis of color stimuli for color matching; the term *color-stimulus synthesis* (CSS) is *operationally* a more strictly accurate term.

a. Color-stimulus synthesis (CSS) may be brought about by spatial or temporal combinations of the energy emitted, reflected, or transmitted by stimulus-objects; this type of synthesis is either an additive or an averaging process.

1. *Additive CSS* may be produced by spatial combinations of stimuli, i.e., by the spatial superposition of the light from a plurality of sources so that each part of the energy-combination stimulates the same portion of the retina. This may be called *spatial-additive CSS* and is most commonly used in visual colorimetry (and assumed in standard systems of color-stimulus specification).

2. *Averaging CSS* is a form of color-stimulus synthesis in which the result is an average of the components rather than the sum.

a) *Spatial-averaging CSS* may be produced by juxtaposition of stimuli (self-luminous or non-self-luminous) that are so small they cannot be individually resolved by the observer.

1) Spatial-averaging CSS by juxtaposition of small stimulus-objects is the basis of modern color television, older systems of additive color photography, and pointillistic painting.

b) *Temporal-averaging CSS* may be produced by the rapid succession or temporal combination of stimuli presented in the same place.

1) When color stimuli are alternated rapidly enough, the colors that would be evoked by the individual stimuli cannot be perceived at all (nor can even a flicker be perceived), but a steady and uniform color results which is

[5.2.2a.2.b)]

different from what would be evoked by the individual component stimuli.

2) The colors resulting from temporal-averaging CSS are related to both the intensity and spectral characteristics of the individual stimuli and the durations of stimulation by each.

3) Temporal-averaging CSS has served as the basis for non-standard systems of color television and some older forms of color motion pictures.

3. A special case of CSS is one in which selected color stimuli that separately produce widely different hue responses are combined to produce an achromatic response; such pairs of stimuli are called *complementary color stimuli,* and the hue responses separately produced by the two members of the pair are called *complementary hues* or, more generally, *complementary colors.*

a) When color samples are arranged in a circle according to the hue responses that they elicit, complementary samples may be placed opposite each other on the circle, so that a line drawn diametrically between them will pass through the center, which represents the neutral achieved by mixing the two stimuli responsible for the complementary colors.

b) In general, yellow hues are complementary to blue hues, blue-green (cyan) hues are complementary to reds, and bluish reds (magentas) are complementary to greens.

b. Color-stimulus synthesis (CSS) may be brought about by the transmission of light through two or more superposed transparent or semitransparent colorants; this is called *subtractive CSS* because each successive colorant decreases the amount of light transmitted [2.1.3b.2.a)].

1. Whenever two or more spectrally selective transmitting substances are combined by superposition, their respective spectral absorptances combine to produce a stimulus-object that transmits light differently from any of the component colorants and, typically, results in the perception of a new and different color [2.1.3b.1.c)].

2. The colorants common to subtractive CSS are usually dyes, and this form of CSS provides the basis for virtually every modern system of color photography and plays a part in many forms of color printing [8.3.4].

c. Additive and averaging CSS have traditionally been referred to as "additive color mixture," and subtractive CSS has traditionally been referred to as "subtractive color mixture," but these terms are misleading if "color" is defined as response. Actually, these terms refer not to color mixture, a synthesis of responses, but to methods of producing color stimuli.

1. In additive CSS, stimulus energies are combined to synthesize a stimulus that always consists of more energy than any of the individual stimulus components.

a) Stimulus energies are combined as the sum of the individual stimulus components in spatial-additive CSS.

2. In spatial-averaging CSS, stimulus energies are combined as a weighted average of the individual component stimuli such that the weighting is a function of spatial factors as well as stimulus energies.

3. In temporal-averaging CSS, stimulus energies are combined in such a manner that the synthesized stimulus is a time-weighted average of the component stimuli. The synthesized stimulus *never* consists of more energy than the component stimulus of highest energy, or of less energy than the component stimulus of least energy, but has a level somewhere in between.

4. In subtractive CSS, stimulus-objects are combined to produce a stimulus that always consists of less energy than any one of the individual stimulus components.

a) Stimulus energies are reduced according to the products of the spectral transmittances of stimulus-objects in subtractive CSS.

5. In general, it may be said that additive CSS adds light to produce responses going from dark to bright, and subtractive CSS subtracts light to produce responses going from bright to dark [Figs. 5.1 and 5.2].

[5.2.2]

d. Stimulus-objects are frequently synthesized by mixtures of colorants (dyes, pigments), and this is referred to as *colorant mixture* [2.1.3b.2.].

1. Stimuli synthesized by colorant mixture may be the result of both spatial-averaging and subtractive CSS, often at the same time.

a) Small colorant particles in juxtaposition in colorant mixture may not be individually resolved by the observer's eye, and the resultant stimulus is then a combination of their reflected energies, or spatial-averaging CSS.
b) Colorant particles may be superimposed, or partially superimposed, and the resultant stimulus synthesized partly according to spatial-averaging CSS and partly according to the amount and kind of their common spectral transmittances, or subtractive CSS.
c) Transparent dye mixtures produce a resultant stimulus by subtractive CSS.

5.3   Basic facts concerning the relations of the components in matching stimuli have been established from color-matching experiments. These facts serve as a basis for *colorimetry.*

5.3.1   Since three independent kinds of variation in the color stimulus are required to match all possible colors, normal color vision is called *trichromatic.*

a. If an observer attempts to match colors by superimposing different amounts of the light from each of several spotlights of different colors on a white screen (spatial-additive CSS), he will find either that three stimuli of different but fixed spectral composition are required, or, if only two lights are used, that not only the amounts of both but also the spectral composition of at least one must be adjustable.
b. If an observer attempts to match colors by temporal-averaging synthesis, for example, with a rotary sector disc, he will find that a minimum of four sectors giving three independent adjustments are necessary to match essentially all colors.
c. If an observer attempts to match colors by adjustment of transparent layers (subtractive synthesis), he will find that a

[5.3.1]

minimum of three dyes is necessary to match essentially all colors.

d. If an observer attempts to match colors by pigment mixture, as in formulating an opaque paint, he will find that a minimum of four paints (one of which may be a "white"), giving three independent adjustments, is necessary to match essentially all colors.

5.3.2 The three (independently variable) chromatic light sources or colorant substances that are necessary to match all colors in a given group are called *primaries.*

a. The choice of primaries in color matching is arbitrary, except for the restriction that no one of the primaries may produce a color which can be matched by any combination of the other two primaries.

b. The primary light sources for additive and for averaging synthesis typically evoke responses of red, green, and blue; hence, red, green, and blue are sometimes referred to as the *additive primaries.*

c. The usual primary colorant substances for subtractive synthesis (and for colorant mixture) typically evoke responses of cyan (blue-green), magenta (blue-red), and yellow; hence, cyan, magenta, and yellow are sometimes referred to as the *subtractive primaries.* Since the subtractive primaries are generally complementary in color to the additive primaries, they are sometimes referred to as minus-red, minus-green, and minus-blue [5.2.2a.3.] [Fig. 3.17].

5.3.3 The outer limit of the *gamut* of stimuli that may be color-matched with any given set of additive primaries is determined by the intensity and wavelength composition of the primary light sources.

a. With any set of real, additive primaries, some colors may be encountered that are too bright to be matched by a synthesis of light from the primaries; this is a limitation of the luminous flux available with that set of primaries, but a color match may be produced either by increasing the luminous output of the primaries or by decreasing the luminance of the sample.

[5.3.3]

b. With any set of real, additive primaries (even single-frequency primaries), some colors may be encountered that are too saturated to be matched by a synthesis of light from the primaries; these colors are said to lie outside the gamut of the particular primary system, but a color match may be produced by adding one or two of the primaries to the color sample.

1. Any color within the gamut of a set of additive primaries may be matched by a synthesis of light from the three primaries.

2. Any color at the edges of the gamut of a set of additive primaries may be matched by a synthesis of light from two of the primaries.

3. Any color outside the gamut of a set of additive primaries may be matched by a synthesis of light from the three primaries only if light from one or two of the primaries is added to the light producing the sample color.

4. Adding light from one of a set of additive primaries to the light producing a sample color is, in effect, the same as subtracting it from the primary synthesis, and this fact gives rise to the concept of *negative amounts of the primaries*.

a) Negative amounts of primaries must be used to match any color that lies outside the normal gamut of colors established by any set of additive primaries.

5.3.4   From information derived from color-matching experiments where the method of three-color additive synthesis was used, a series of basic principles about color matching has been derived; these principles have been referred to as *"Grassman's laws"* since they were first stated by him in 1853 (99).

a. Color stimuli are characterized by only three independent kinds of differences or variation.

b. If one component of a two-component additive synthesis is steadily changed (while the other remains constant), the color produced by the synthesis changes in a corresponding manner.

c. Stimuli evoking the same color produce identical effects in additive syntheses regardless of their spectral compositions.

d.   When two stimuli evoking the same color are added respectively to two other stimuli which also produce matching colors, the resulting additive syntheses will produce a color match. (This is parallel to the algebraic axiom that "if equals are added to equals the results are equal.")

e. When two stimuli evoking the same color are subtracted respectively from two other stimuli that also produce matching colors, the remainders will produce a color match. (This is parallel to the algebraic axiom that "if equals are subtracted from equals, the results are equal.")

f. Over a wide range, increasing or decreasing in the same ratio, the intensity of two stimuli that evoke the same color will not destroy the color match, regardless of the spectral composition of the two stimuli. (This is parallel to the algebraic axiom that "if equals are multiplied—or divided—by equals, the results are equal.")

1. A proportionate increase or decrease in the intensity of two stimuli that evoke a color match may destroy the color match if the field size, field luminance, and surround luminance are such as to permit rod vision to intrude.

2. A proportionate increase or decrease in the intensity of two stimuli that evoke a color match may destroy the color match when the intensity of stimulation approaches a level high enough to interfere with the usual nutritive processes of the retina; this may occur at luminances of more than 10 thousand foot-lamberts or as low as 1 thousand foot-lamberts under special circumstances.

g. Grassman's laws have traditionally been referred to as the *"laws of color mixture,"* and they serve as the basis for the science of colorimetry.

1. A term preferred to "laws of color mixture" is *"laws of additive CSS,"* for it is specifically on the facts of additive synthesis that the science of colorimetry is based.

5.3.5 It is possible to represent color syntheses either graphically, numerically, or in vector notation.

a. If three additive primaries are represented by the apices of a triangle, and proportionate amounts of the light from each primary are represented along axes normal to the sides opposite

[5.3.5a.]

the apices, the quality of any color stimulus resulting from a synthesis of light from the primaries can be represented at the point within the triangle indicated by the respective proportions of the primaries in the synthesis. This quality of the color stimulus is called *chromaticity,* and the triangular diagram is called a *chromaticity diagram.* This is the graphical representation of color syntheses.

1. If, for example, half a unit of one primary is added to half a unit of another, the chromaticity of the stimulus so synthesized will be represented on the line connecting the two primary points and will be midway between them; or, in general terms, chromaticity points for sums of the primaries in any proportions may be found by the center-of-gravity principle, where the amounts of the primaries serve as analogs of the masses.

2. The concept of representing the chromaticities produced by additive CSS by points on a chromaticity diagram through use of the center-of-gravity principle is known as *Newton's Law of Color Mixture.*

b. If the amounts of the primaries required to match a color stimulus are *R*, *G*, *B*, these amounts give the numerical specification of the color-stimulus synthesis. If these amounts are normalized to unit sum, they are called *chromaticity coordinates* and constitute the numerical specification of the quality of the color stimulus synthesis.

c. If unit amounts of the primaries are taken to define unit vectors, **R**, **G**, **B**, the color-stimulus synthesis, **C**, may be considered as the vector sum of *R* units of vector **R**, *G* units of vector **G**, and *B* units of vector **B**, thus:

$$\mathbf{C} \equiv R\mathbf{R} + G\mathbf{G} + B\mathbf{B},$$

where $\equiv$ means "equivalent to."

Chapter Six

Colorimetry

Color, as visual response, is usually not measured directly. "Color measurement" often refers only to the measurement of characteristics of the color stimulus, and a color-stimulus specification in its most fundamental form relates measured characteristics of the color stimulus to the calculated response of a standard observer. The techniques of such specification comprise colorimetry (49, 93, 242, 293).

6.1 Color, as a visual response, is directly amenable to specification but is usually represented, for a given perceptual situation, by derived functions which describe stimulus relations required to produce equality of color or color difference.

6.1.1 *Derived functions* represent relations between measurable quantities but do not evaluate those quantities themselves.

a. In physics, the concepts of velocity and acceleration, for example, are derived functions relating position (or distance) and time, but numbers representing velocity or acceleration do not tell us directly anything about the magnitudes of either distance (position) or time. Similarly, amounts of primaries required to match a color stimulus are derived functions expressing equality of color response, but they do not evaluate either the magnitude or the quality of that response.

6.1.2 An invariance in color response (e.g., a given constant color difference or an equality of color responses) may be rep-

[6.1.2]

resented, for a given perceptual situation, by derived stimulus constructs; such derived relations are called *psychophysical functions* or *psychophysical specifications*.

a. A psychophysical specification, comprising, for example, a pair of chromaticity coordinates and a luminance value, represents the relation in which a set of stimulus parameters must stand in order to obtain equality of responses elicited by two juxtaposed fields.

b. A psychophysical function comprising, for example, the change in wavelength as a function of wavelength required to produce a just-perceptible difference in color under a given set of viewing conditions, represents only the differences in stimulus parameters required to obtain a constant difference between the responses elicited by the stimuli.

c. *Colorimetric specifications* are psychophysical specifications which provide a method of stating stimulus conditions required to obtain a constant *relationship* of color responses (equality or difference).

6.1.3 Variations in color response as a function of stimulation may be specified in terms of an observer's reports of his judgments concerning the magnitudes of his responses; scales of response may be determined on the basis of direct magnitude or ratio estimates or on the basis of categorical position or equality of intervals.

a. Color measurements provide a method of describing the growth of response as a function of stimulation.

b. Specifications of the absolute or relative magnitudes of response along dimensions of hue, saturation, and brightness are specifications of color (in terms of direct judgment by the sensing observer) and should not be confused with the more common but more restrictive psychophysical specifications of the color stimulus.

6.2 A particular color response has no *unique* relation to a particular color stimulus.

6.2.1 Since the *same* color response can be aroused by a *variety* of color stimuli, the ideal method for measuring color would be one in which responses are ordered along dimensions correspond-

[6.2]

ing to *hue, saturation,* and *brightness,* and in which all stimulus configurations in all their aspects (spatial, temporal, spectral, etc.) producing a given response could be related to that response.

6.2.2 Ideally, a complete specification of the relationship between a color stimulus and a color response should take the form of an equation in which response, R, and *all* factors, S_i, leading to that response are represented respectively as follows:

$$R = f(S_1, S_2, S_3, \ldots, S_n)$$

or, since a color response is tridimensional,

$$(R_1, R_2, R_3) = f(S_1, S_2, S_3, \ldots, S_n)$$

6.2.3 The factors that determine a color *response* are principally the energy characteristics of the stimulus object; the general level and quality of adaptation of the sensing observer; the size and duration of the stimulus; the number, size, and energy characteristics of other objects in the field of view; the absorption characteristics of the ocular media; and binocular interactions.

6.2.4 No system of specification has ever taken into account all the stimulus factors that determine a color response.

6.3 *Colorimetry* is defined as the technique of measuring color stimuli to provide a system of color-stimulus specification.

6.3.1 In colorimetry, a system of color-stimulus specification has been developed which relates certain stimulus characteristics to the calculated response of a standardized average observer, based on the fact that in any one given set of viewing conditions, any color stimulus may be matched by a unique mixture of three appropriately different color stimuli. The match will then be one in which the reference field elicits the same calculated response as that resulting from the sample. This is a very useful convention even though it may not predict correctly the match of any actual observer. Although the specification may relate to the color of the sample, it is not sufficient to determine it.

6.3.2 A stimulus-response system was adopted in 1931 by the Commission Internationale d'Éclairage (CIE) as the international standard for colorimetric specification (49).

   a. The term "color" has not been formally defined by the CIE.

   b. In spite of the fact that the term "color" has never been de-

[6.3.2b.]

fined by the CIE, it is frequently implied in technical reports concerned with the CIE system of color specification that the term "color" refers to the stimulus characteristics specified by the CIE system.

1. The Optical Society of America and the Illuminating Engineering Society (U.S.A.) have both defined color as the aspect of the stimulus specified by dominant wavelength, purity, and luminance, which is essentially equivalent to a specification representing the mathematical relation between a stimulus and the related response of a standard observer (201).

c. According to OSA and IES definitions of color, a particular "color" may lead to many different appearances, depending on the viewing conditions.

d. For consistency in this report, the term "color-stimulus specification" or "CIE specification" is used to refer to "color" as defined by the OSA and IES, so that the report definition of color may be retained as having response implications.

6.3.3 There are several conventions to which the CIE system is committed by resolution.

a. Three standard sources are defined for the CIE system; Sources A, B, and C [Fig. 6.1] (49).

1. *CIE Source A* consists of a gas-filled incandescent lamp operating at 2854°K.

a) The spectral energy distribution of CIE Source A is defined as that of a black body at 2854°K, with C_2 of Planck's radiation formula set at 14,380 micron-degrees.

b) The original CIE specification for Source A was 2848°K, with C_2 at 14,350, and this figure may appear in some texts. A more recent convention, however, ascribes a color temperature of 2854°K ($C_2 = 14,380$) to Source A. In either case, regardless of the convention applied to compute the number representing the color temperature, the spectral distribution of the source is the same.

c) CIE Source A is intended to represent common tungsten filament light sources.

[6.3.3a.]

2. *CIE Source B* comprises the lamp specified as Source A in combination with a special filter to produce a spectral distribution that approximates noon sunlight.

a) CIE Source B has a correlated color temperature of 4870°K.

b) The actual energy distribution of CIE Source B is specified and tabulated at 10 mμ intervals from 380 mμ to 780 mμ.

3. *CIE Source C* comprises the lamp specified as Source A in combination with a special filter to produce a spectral distribution that approximates daylight (sunlight plus skylight).

a) CIE Source C has a correlated color temperature of 6740°K.

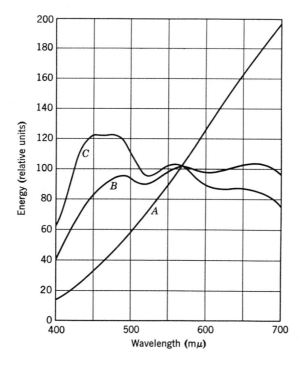

Fig. 6.1 Relative energy distributions of CIE standard illuminants A, B, and C (Committee on Colorimetry, 1944c, p. 635).

[6.3.3a.3.]

b) Originally, CIE Source C was intended to have a color temperature of about 6500°K, and this figure may appear in some texts. A more recent convention, however, ascribes a correlated color temperature of 6740°K to Source C. In either case, the spectral distribution of the source is the same.

c) The actual spectral energy distribution of CIE Source C is specified and tabulated at 10 mμ intervals from 380 mμ to 780 mμ.

b. *Standard viewing conditions* are defined for the CIE system.

1. The color matches on which the CIE observer is based were obtained by viewing a circular bipartite field, subtending a visual angle of 2°, in an otherwise dark field.

2. The CIE system recommends that reflecting materials be illuminated at an angle of 45° and viewed at an angle of 90° (normal) to the surface; but any other angular conditions may be used if they are noted as part of the specification.

3. In practice, CIE specifications are used for specifying a color match under a wide variety of viewing conditions; such specifications may be outside the range of actual observed values if the field subtense is less than $\frac{1}{2}$° or more than 4°, if the luminance is less than 0.1 or more than 1,000 foot-lamberts, or if the radiant energy from the color stimulus falls on a retinal area other than the fovea or parafovea. Such specifications are sometimes used in default of any other recognized specification.

c. Based on the fact that any color can be matched by a unique CSS of three appropriately different color stimuli, a *CIE specification* is given by a set of three numbers which represent the match for the CIE standard observer.

1. In the CIE system, the three numbers chosen for a color-stimulus specification may take one of several forms, all of which are related.

a) One set of three numbers that may be used for color-stimulus specification consists of what are called *tristimulus values*.

[6.3.3c.1.a)]

1) The CIE tristimulus values represent a particular mathematical transformation from a set of three real primaries to three non-real primaries for reasons of computational convenience [Figs. 6.2 and 6.3] [5.3.2].

(a) CIE tristimulus values are denoted as X, Y, and Z and represent the relative amounts of the non-real primary color stimuli of the CIE system required to match some color stimulus whose specification they represent.

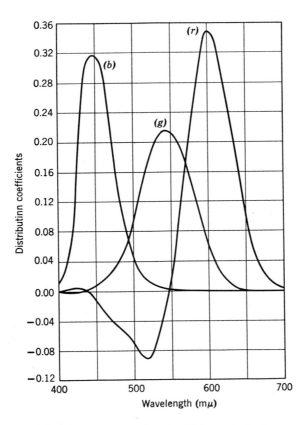

Fig. 6.2 Spectral distribution curves for the CIE standard observer and monochromatic primaries at the wavelengths 700 mμ, 546.1 mμ, and 435.8 mμ (Smith and Guild, 1931–1932, pp. 94–95).

[6.3.3c.1.a)1)]

(b) CIE tristimulus values are obtained mathematically by evaluating the effect on the standard observer's eye of spectral flux, either directly from a light source or as it is reflected or transmitted by an object.

(1) CIE tristimulus values for objects are defined as follows:

$$X = \frac{\int_0^\infty \bar{x}(\lambda)P(\lambda)\rho(\lambda)\,d\lambda}{\int_0^\infty \bar{y}(\lambda)P(\lambda)\,d\lambda}$$

$$Y = \frac{\int_0^\infty \bar{y}(\lambda)P(\lambda)\rho(\lambda)\,d\lambda}{\int_0^\infty \bar{y}(\lambda)P(\lambda)\,d\lambda}$$

$$Z = \frac{\int_0^\infty \bar{z}(\lambda)P(\lambda)\rho(\lambda)\,d\lambda}{\int_0^\infty \bar{y}(\lambda)P(\lambda)\,d\lambda}$$

where $\bar{x}$, $\bar{y}$, $\bar{z}$ are functions (often called *distribution functions*) representing the amounts of the CIE primaries required by the standard observer to color match narrow bands of wavelengths throughout the visible spectrum, with equal energy presented for all bands [Fig. 6.3].
P is the spectral radiant flux from the light source illuminating an object.
ρ is the spectral reflectance or transmittance of the object.
λ represents wavelength.

2) Regardless of spectral composition, all color stimuli producing the same calculated response for the standard observer have identical tristimulus values X, Y, and Z; two such color stimuli are said to form a *metameric pair*

[6.3.3c.1.a)]

of their spectral distributions are different, or an *isomeric pair* if their distributions are the same.

3) The mathematical transformation used to define the CIE tristimulus values produces a numerical system in which only positive numbers are required for the specification of all colors.

4) The transformation used to define the CIE tristimulus values was intended to produce a tristimulus value Y which would be a valid correlate for brightness by making Y equal to luminance [Fig. 6.4].

(a) Luminance is not linearly related to brightness (23, 118, 123, 126, 174, 203), particularly at the brightness extremes.

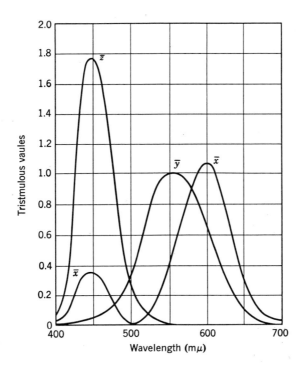

Fig. 6.3   CIE tristimulus values $\bar{x}$, $\bar{y}$, and $\bar{z}$ for the spectrum colors (Committee on Colorimetry, 1944, p. 642).

[6.3.3c.1.a)4)]

(b) For any one of various viewing situations, luminance is not simply related to brightness, particularly for colors of high saturation (30, 43, 70, 175, 235, 236, 237, 255, 266, 295, 296).

(c) Over a limited range of tristimulus values, luminance (tristimulus value Y) may be considered to be an approximate correlate for brightness.

(d) In the CIE system, luminance (Y) is evaluated in terms of the calculated response of the standard observer to the spectral radiance of the test field.

(e) In the CIE system, the luminous reflectance (relative luminance) of an opaque (reflecting) material is expressed relative to the luminance of a magnesium oxide surface under the same conditions of illumination.

(f) In the CIE system, *luminance* may be expressed as the Y tristimulus value, or in related photometric

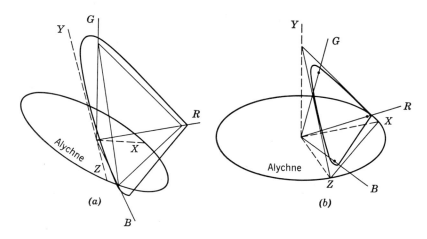

Fig. 6.4   Schematic representation of the vector systems of (a) an additive CSS system consisting of real primaries, and (b) an additive CSS system consisting of nonreal primaries such as the CIE system.   The plane of zero luminance (the alychne) has been transformed mathematically in (b) such that the X and Z primaries lie on it.   Hence only the Y dimension contains luminance information.   In addition, the locus of chromaticities corresponding to spectral energy is found to lie within the gamut of the nonreal X, Y, and Z primaries.   From Murray, H. D., *Colour in Theory and Practice*, London: Chapman & Hall, Ltd., 1952, Fig. 11.6, p. 136.

[6.3.3c.1.]

units such as millilamberts, foot-lamberts, or candles per square meter [5.1.6].

b) A second set of three numbers that may be used for CIE specification includes two *chromaticity coordinates* and the *luminance* information provided by the Y tristimulus value.

1) Chromaticity coordinates are denoted as x, y, and z, and any pair of them together with Y may be used to complete a CIE specification; usually x and y are used, although x and z are sometimes used in European countries.

2) Chromaticity coordinates are computed directly from tristimulus values, and are defined as

$$x = \frac{X}{X + Y + Z}$$

$$y = \frac{Y}{X + Y + Z}$$

$$z = \frac{Z}{X + Y + Z}$$

3) Since the sum of the CIE chromaticity coordinates is unity $(x + y + z = 1)$, a knowledge of any two of them leads to the value of the third merely by subtracting the sum of the two known values from 1. Therefore, only two chromaticity coordinates are required with Y to give a full CIE specification.

4) Since only two chromaticity coordinates are needed with Y to give a complete CIE specification, the two coordinates (usually x and y) may be plotted on a graph, and the Y values can be written as a number next to the (x, y) point plotted on the graph to complete the specification.

(a) A graph of the CIE chromaticity coordinates (x, y) for all CIE specifications is called the CIE *chromaticity diagram*, and the characteristic specified by (x, y) is called chromaticity.

[6.3.3c.1.b)]

    5) When the chromaticities for single-frequency light are plotted in a chromaticity diagram and joined by a curved line, the *spectrum locus* is determined; a straight line drawn to connect the chromaticities for the two ends of the spectrum locus (longest and shortest wavelengths) creates a closed figure within which the *chromaticities* for all physically attainable color stimuli will fall [Fig. 6.5].

c) A third set of three numbers that may be used for CIE specification is made up of *dominant wavelength* (λ_D), *excitation purity* (P_e), and *luminance* (Y).

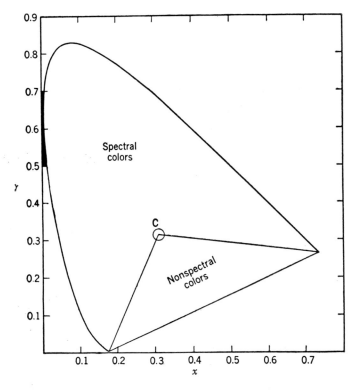

Fig. 6.5 Division of real chromaticities into spectral and nonspectral parts. From Judd, D. B., *Color in Business, Science, and Industry*, New York: John Wiley & Sons, Inc., 1952, Fig. 34, p. 130.

[6.3.3c.1.c)]

1) The dominant wavelength of a CIE specification is determined by drawing a line on the CIE chromaticity diagram between the chromaticity point of a reference source and the chromaticity point of the sample and extending the line until it intersects the spectrum locus. The wavelength at which the line intersects the spectrum locus is called the *dominant wavelength* of the sample.

(a) Dominant wavelength is the CIE specification most closely related to hue, but a line of constant dominant wavelength does not correspond to constant hue [Fig. 6.6].

(b) In the case of non-spectral color stimuli that produce purples and magentas, and which can be produced only by a mixture of light of long and short wavelengths, a *complementary wavelength* (λc) is specified by extending the line which joins the chromaticity points of the sample and the reference source beyond the chromaticity for the source to the spectrum locus.

(c) Since dominant wavelength is referred to a given

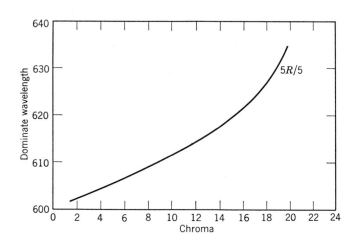

Fig. 6.6 Dominant wavelength as a function of Munsell Chroma (correlate of saturation) for samples of constant Hue and Value (correlate of lightness). Although the hue of the samples is constant, their dominant wavelengths vary according to saturation.

[6.3.3c.1.c)]

reference source, the dominant wavelength of a sample is usually different for different reference sources.

2) The *excitation purity*, or simply *purity*, of a CIE specification is the ratio of two distances along a line of dominant wavelength.

(a) The *excitation purity* of a CIE specification is the ratio of the distance between the chromaticity point of the reference source and that of the sample to the distance between the chromaticity point of the source and the point on the spectrum locus representing the dominant wavelength of the sample.

(1) For purples and magentas, the line used to compute excitation purity is not a line of dominant wavelength but one extended from the chromaticity point of the reference source through the chromaticity point of the sample and on to the non-spectral boundary that connects the chromaticity points of the long- and short-wave ends of the spectrum.

(b) The excitation purity of a CIE specification may be computed from the following equation:

$$P_e = \frac{x - x_a}{x_b - x_a} = \frac{y - y_a}{y_b - y_a}$$

where P_e represents excitation purity,

x, y define the chromaticity point of the sample,

x_a, y_a define the chromaticity point of the light source, and

x_b, y_b define the chromaticity point on the spectrum locus or the non-spectral boundary.

(Note: The form of the equation that has the the larger denominator should be used.)

(c) Excitation purity is the CIE specification most closely related to saturation, but equal purities in different parts of the chromaticity diagram do not correspond to equal saturations [Fig. 6.7].

(d) A second kind of purity, called *colorimetric purity* (P_c), is sometimes used in colorimetry [2.1.2d.3.].

[6.3.3c.1.c)2)(d)]

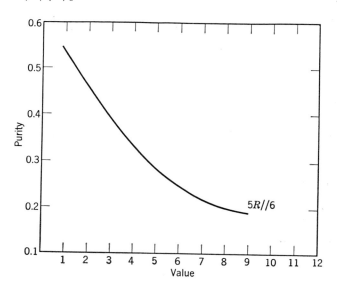

Fig. 6.7   Excitation purity as a function of Munsell Value (correlate of lightness) for samples of constant Hue and Chroma (correlate of saturation). Although the saturation of the samples remains constant, the excitation purity depends upon lightness.

(1) *Colorimetric purity* is by definition the ratio of the luminance of the spectrally pure component to the luminance of the matching mixture.

(2) Colorimetric purity may be derived from CIE chromaticities and is related to excitation purity by the following equation:

$$P_c = \frac{y_b}{y} (P_e)$$

$$= \frac{y_b}{y} \left(\frac{x - x_a}{x_b - x_a} \right) = \frac{y_b}{y} \left(\frac{y - y_a}{y_b - y_a} \right)$$

where the symbols are the same as those in [6.3.3c.1.c)2)(b)].

6.3.4   Colorimetry may be accomplished by the use of either visual or physical colorimeters or by direct stimulus measurement

[6.3.4]

(such as spectrophotometry and spectroradiometry) combined with computation in a system of color specification like the CIE, which is based on color matching [6.9].

    a. *Photometry* is a limited case of colorimetry; it is the process of measuring emitted, reflected, or transmitted energy and expressing these quantities in luminous terms.

        1. Photometry is generally considered to be a process of visual comparison; i.e., the visual mechanism itself is used as the receptor element in photometric measuring devices (photometers).

        2. *Physical photometers* sometimes are used to produce data that can be related to the calculated response of a standard observer.

6.4 Distances in the CIE chromaticity diagram do not correspond to uniform visual intervals and therefore give a very poor indication of the stimulus difference required for color discrimination.

    6.4.1 Numerous attempts to determine a mathematical transformation of the CIE coordinate system into one in which equal distances correspond to equal visual intervals have been made with more or less success.

    6.4.2 Any attempt to represent visually uniform intervals in a color space must be based on an empirical determination of the relations between color stimuli and responses under a given set of viewing conditions.

        a. The renotation of the Munsell Color System [8.3.3c.] represents an experimental determination of equal visual intervals, as well as the object-color samples required to produce them, with illumination by CIE Source C on a uniform surround anywhere between middle gray and white [Fig. 6.8] (205).

        b. The objective of the Munsell renotation was to derive a psychological color solid in which cylindrical coordinates in Euclidean space represent the dimensions of color perceived as belonging to surfaces and in which equal distances represent perceptually equal color differences.

        c. Although the Munsell renotation represents a color solid which approaches more closely than any other available object-

[6.4.2c.]

color system the ideal of a perceptually uniform Euclidean color space, it is not a completely successful model.

1. It has been shown theoretically, and substantiated empirically, that for a particular observing condition no simple

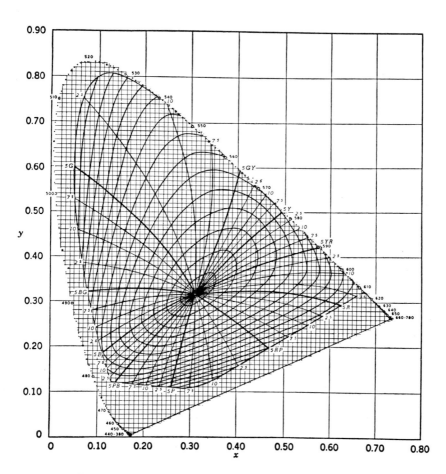

Fig. 6.8 Chromaticities of ideal Munsell colors, Value 5/, shown on the (x,y)-chromaticity diagram. This chart serves to define Munsell renotation Hue and Chroma for colors having $Y/Y_0 = 0.198$. (Prepared by Color Measurement Laboratory, War Food Administration, U.S.D.A.) From Judd, D. B., *Color in Business, Science, and Industry*, New York: John Wiley & Sons, Inc., 1952, Fig. 69, p. 233.

[6.4.2c.]

Euclidean space can be used to represent a perfectly uniform color space (159, 246).

2. As a result of the empirical evaluations and adjustments
used in deriving the Munsell renotation, the *chroma* (correlate of saturation) and *value* (correlate of lightness) scales
represent better dimensional "fits" to a uniform perceptual
space than does the Munsell *hue* scale.

3. In the Munsell renotation, value scales were adjusted at
neutral and near-neutral levels, and then all other samples at
a given Y tristimulus value were arbitrarily assigned the same
Munsell value [6.3.3c.1.a)].

a) It has been shown that surfaces which produce constant lightness do not lie in planes of constant luminous
reflectance (tristimulus value *Y*), especially at high saturations [6.3.3c.1.a)4)(b)] [Fig. 6.9].

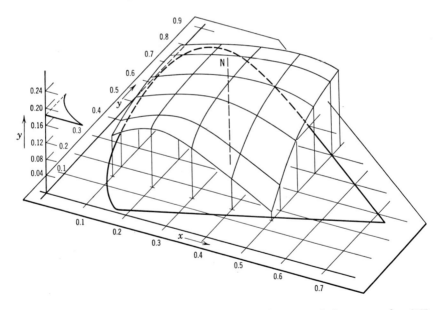

Fig. 6.9 Axonometric projection of a surface of constant lightness in the CIE
chromaticity-luminance space. The luminance required for equal lightness is
seen to decrease as a function of increasing purity. From Sanders, C. L., and
Wyszecki, G., Correlate for Lightness in Terms of C.I.E. Tristimulus Values,
Part I., *J. opt. Soc. Amer.*, 1957, *47*, 398–404 (Fig. 9, p. 403).

[6.4.2]

d. All the color stimuli produced by the samples of known Munsell renotation illuminated by CIE Source C are specified in the CIE system and so can be plotted on CIE chromaticity diagrams.

1. Any color stimulus of known CIE specification can be evaluated in terms of Munsell renotation by interpolation on CIE chromaticity diagrams on which the contours of constant Munsell hue and Munsell chroma are plotted.

6.5 It is possible to measure color appearance for single stimuli in simple fields and to predict shifts in color from one kind of adaptation to another (40, 292).

6.5.1 If a color stimulus for any adaptive condition is found to produce the same color as a second color stimulus for the standard "Munsell adaptive conditions," then the Munsell renotation of the second stimulus gives an evaluation of the color produced by the first stimulus, valid to the extent that the Munsell hue, value, and chroma of the color stimulus correlates with the hue, saturation, and lightness of the color.

6.5.2 A procedure for approximately predicting color shifts with a change in adaptation from one source to another was outlined by von Kries (169) and has been experimentally verified (51, 93, 292). This procedure is based on von Kries' coefficient law.

a. The *von Kries coefficient law* states that the color-response functions of the eye ($\bar{r}$, $\bar{g}$, $\bar{b}$) under one set of adaptation conditions may be considered to be proportional to the response functions ($\bar{r}'$, $\bar{g}'$, $\bar{b}'$) under another set of adaptation conditions,

$$\bar{r}' = k_r\bar{r}, \; \bar{g}' = k_g\bar{g}, \; \bar{b}' = k_b\bar{b}$$

6.5.3 Many extensions of the von Kries coefficient law have been proposed in attempts to predict precisely the changes in appearance of color stimuli when conditions of adaptation are varied, but none has been completely successful (2, 3, 24, 27, 40, 46, 49, 86, 92, 93, 113, 119, 123, 124, 125, 126, 127, 138, 140, 147, 149, 157, 159, 203, 221, 232, 270, 293).

6.6 *One-dimensional scales* of colorimetric specification are sometimes used for special applications where variation in color is produced as a function of some single physical variable.

[6.6]

6.6.1 A color-temperature scale is a one-dimensional scale of colorimetric specification based on the chromaticity change produced for complete thermal radiators by a change of temperature; the scale is accurately applicable to any radiator having any of the chromaticities of black bodies, which are referred to as Planckian radiators [Fig. 6.10].

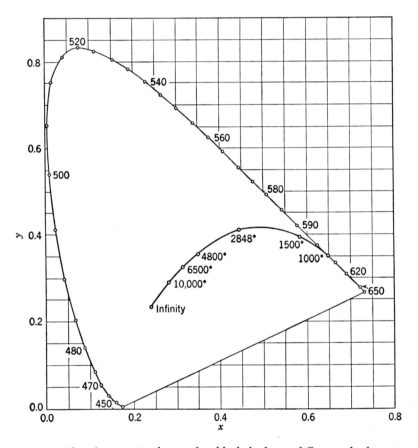

Fig. 6.10 The chromaticity locus of a black body at different absolute temperatures. As the temperature increases, the chromaticity proceeds along the curve towards infinity. From Evans, R. M., *An Introduction to Color,* New York: John Wiley & Sons, Inc., 1948, Fig. 13-12, p. 214.

[6.6.1]

a. Color temperature is a specification of chromaticity along a single curved line (called the Planckian locus) in a chromaticity diagram, and is not a specification of spectral energy distribution (although a spectral energy distribution is often wrongly implied).

b. *Color temperature* is defined as the temperature in degrees Kelvin of a totally absorbing or *black body* (non-selective radiator) which produces the chromaticity to be specified.

1. The color temperature of a non-selective radiator is the same as its absolute temperature.

2. The color temperature of a slightly selective radiator may be either higher or lower than its absolute temperature, e.g., the color temperatures of incandescent tungsten filaments are higher than their absolute temperatures.

3. The chromaticity of a significantly selective radiator, such as a fluorescent lamp, is sometimes specified in terms of *correlated color temperature*.

a) Correlated color temperature is the temperature of the Planckian radiator which produces the chromaticity most similar to that produced by the selective radiator in question.

b) The loci of constant correlated color temperatures, *isotemperature loci*, and their *conjunctive wavelengths* (the wavelengths at which the isotemperature loci intersect the spectrum locus) have been defined in the Judd uniform chromaticity diagram, but since Judd's diagram has not been adopted as a standard, correlated color temperature must be considered as a provisional approximation [Fig. 6.11] (156).

c. Color temperatures are sometimes expressed on a reciprocal scale ($10^6/T$) whose units are *micro-reciprocal degrees* (μrd), sometimes also abbreviated as *mireds*.

1. Equal distances on the mired scale represent approximately equal visual differences, i.e., over the range of 0 to 1000, one mired corresponds approximately to a just-noticeable color difference (155, 156).

[6.6.1c.]

2. An optical *conversion* filter (used to vary the color temperature of a radiator) that changes the reciprocal color temperature by a given amount at one point on the color temperature scale will change it by nearly the same amount at any other point on the scale; hence, the mired often is used

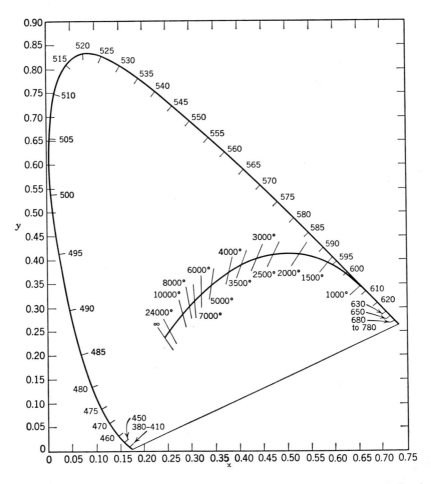

Fig. 6.11 CIE chromaticity diagram showing locus of chromaticities of Planckian radiators and lines of constant correlated color temperature. From Committee on Colorimetry, Optical Society of America, *The Science of Color*, New York: Thomas Y. Crowell Co., 1953, Fig. 80, p. 304.

[6.6.1c.2.]

to specify the color-temperature-altering power of conversion filters.

6.6.2 While color temperature probably is the most singularly important one-dimensional scale of colorimetric specification, there are other such scales designed for specialized purposes. These usually take the form of collections of material color samples [8.6].

6.7 As a basis for specification in colorimetry, the technique of measuring color stimuli without regard to the color response is accomplished by several techniques: spectroradiometry, spectrophotometry, radiometry, and physical photometry.

6.7.1 *Spectroradiometry* is the measurement of the *spectral radiance* of direct radiators (self-luminous stimulus-objects) and provides a measure of the rate at which energy is radiated in a given direction by a source at every wavelength within the range under consideration [2.1.3a.].

6.7.2 *Spectrophotometry* refers to the measurement of radiant flux reflected or transmitted by non-self-luminous stimulus-objects at each wavelength within the range under consideration [2.1.3b.].

6.7.3 *Radiometry* refers to measurement of the absolute rate at which energy is emitted by a direct radiator without regard to wavelength.

6.7.4 *Physical photometry* refers to measurement of luminous flux, without regard to wavelength, by physical detectors whose spectral sensitivity approximates that of the human eye.

6.7.5 Spectrophotometric and spectroradiometric data are useful in systems of colorimetric specification such as the CIE system, but they do not, in themselves, provide either a measure or specification of color; they constitute measures of the stimulus only.

6.8 The instruments used in measurements of the color stimulus are comprised basically of two components: a device for isolating narrow bands of wavelengths of light and a radiation detector or photoreceptor which responds to some aspect of the energy [Fig. 6.12].

6.8.1 In measurements of the color stimulus, it is usually first necessary to isolate narrow bands of wavelengths.

[6.8.1]

a. Before narrow bands of wavelengths may be isolated, light must be *dispersed* according to wavelength into a spectrum [2.1.3b.4.].

b. Devices for dispersing light usually embody *prisms* or *diffraction gratings* for the purpose.

   1. A *prism* is an object (usually made from glass when a spectrum of light is required) which has plane, non-parallel surfaces that serve to refract a beam of light and disperse it into a spectrum.

   2. A *diffraction grating*, in its most simple form, is an opaque screen containing a large number of very narrow transparent rulings equally spaced. Light incident upon the grating is "bent" around these obstacles, i.e., each of the rulings may be considered to be a secondary source from which light radiates in all directions. This is called *diffraction*. The refracted light by constructive and destructive interference forms a series of spectra (first order, second order, etc.) [2.1.3b.4.c)].

   3. Broad and sometimes narrow bands of wavelengths may be isolated by optical filters that selectively absorb or reflect a

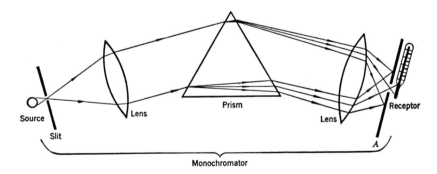

Fig. 6.12   Diagram of a basic instrument for measuring color stimuli. Light passes through a slit, a lens, is dispersed by a prism, and with the aid of a second slit and lens may be isolated and monitored by a photoreceptor. From Evans, R. M., *An Introduction to Color*, New York: John Wiley & Sons, Inc., 1948, p. 10.

[6.8.1]

portion of the incident energy and transmit the rest of that energy.

c. A device commonly used in measurements of color stimuli is a *monochromator.*

1. A monochromator is an optical device which serves to disperse light into a spectrum and, with suitable optics, permits isolation of narrow and continuously variable bands of wavelengths.
2. *Prisms* or *gratings* are used in monochromators as a means of dispersion.
3. Monochromators constitute the dispersing device incorporated into *spectrophotometers* and *spectroradiometers.*
4. The American Standards Association's standard method for color measurement (Z58.71-1951) specifies for monochromators a nominal bandwidth of 10 millimicrons.

a) According to the ASA, the location of a spectral band in the spectrum is described by its *"spectral centroid,"* defined as

$$\lambda c = \frac{\int \lambda \cdot S_\lambda \cdot P_\lambda \cdot d\lambda}{\int S_\lambda \cdot P_\lambda \cdot d\lambda}$$

where S_λ = spectral sensitivity of the receptor at wavelength λ, and P_λ = the relative amount of flux in the band at λ.

6.8.2 In measurements of the color stimulus, after narrow bands of wavelengths have been isolated, a radiation detector or *photoreceptor* (or simply receptor) is then used to measure the flux in the narrow bands.

a. Photoreceptors may be either *human visual receptors* or *physical receptors.*

1. The visual mechanism cannot distinguish the various wavelengths of light that comprise a color stimulus, nor can it easily quantify any aspect of energy (flux, radiance, irradiance) in absolute terms. For this reason the eye is generally used as a photoreceptor only in *null* or *comparative* instruments.

[6.8.2a.1.]

a) The spectral sensitivity of the visual mechanism varies considerably from one observer to another.

2. Physical photoreceptors, or radiation detectors, are classed generally as either thermal detectors or quantum detectors.

a) In *thermal detectors*, radiant energy is absorbed and transformed into heat, producing a temperature rise in the device. Thermal detectors are usually classed as *bolometers*, *thermocouples* (and *thermopiles*), or *pneumatic detectors*.
b) In *quantum detectors*, the incident quanta of light (photons) change the physical characteristics of the device directly. Quantum detectors may be classed as *photoemissive*, *photoconductive*, *photovoltaic*, or *photographic*.

3. Physical receptors may be calibrated either in absolute units or in relative units.

6.9 The instruments most commonly used for measurements of the color stimulus are spectroradiometers, spectrophotometers, colorimeters, and photometers.

6.9.1 *Spectroradiometers* are used for measuring the rate at which energy at each wavelength throughout the spectrum is emitted by direct radiators; they are used for measuring spectral radiances above and below as well as within the spectrum of light. Since spectroradiometers measure absolute radiant flux, spectroradiometric measurements are expressed in such units as ergs per second, watts, and microwatts.

a. Basically, a spectroradiometer comprises a *monochromator* and a *physical photoreceptor* (but never a visual receptor) calibrated in terms of absolute units of radiant flux.
b. Maintaining an accurate calibration for a spectroradiometer is a difficult task and for this reason spectroradiometers are not as commonly used as other instruments which demand somewhat less precise control and calibration.
c. The need for *direct* measurements of spectral radiances is usually circumvented in colorimetric practice through the use of standard light sources for which tables of spectral radiance are readily available.

[6.9]

6.9.2 *Spectrophotometers* are used for measuring the spectral reflectances or transmittances of indirect radiators, and while they are sometimes used for measuring these quantities at wavelengths beyond the spectrum of light, their usefulness for colorimetry lies in the fact that highly precise and accurate measurements can be made of the rate of flow of reflected or transmitted energy relative to the rate of incidence throughout the spectrum of light.

a. Basically, a spectrophotometer comprises a *monochromator* and a *photoreceptor* (usually physical) with an associated comparator by means of which the reflected or transmitted flux may be compared with the incident flux.

1. Spectrophotometers are typically null or comparative instruments and their outputs are related to percent reflectance or transmittance.

b. *Abridged spectrophotometers* are devices in which the reflectance or transmittance of a sample is measured for a number of fixed bands of wavelengths.

1. Abridged spectrophotometers are useful when neither high accuracy nor continuously variable wavelength is necessary or where the critical spectral energy parameters of an object are known and it is desirable only to measure reflectance or transmittance at these points in the spectrum.
2. A *color densitometer* is a form of abridged spectrophotometer used in color photography and the graphic arts. A densitometer typically measures radiant flux for three narrow bands of wavelengths isolated by optical filters at or near the wavelengths of peak absorption of the colorants used in a particular system of color reproduction.

6.9.3 *Colorimeters* do not measure the color stimulus directly, but known fixed stimuli are mixed in appropriate amounts to match a sample stimulus, and the matching mixture may be expressed as a colorimetric specification.

a. Colorimeters typically produce a matching mixture by spatial-additive synthesis, in which case they are called *additive colorimeters* [5.2.2a.].
b. Colorimeters may produce a matching mixture by spatial-

[6.9.3]

or temporal-averaging synthesis, in which case they may be referred to as *averaging colorimeters* [5.2.2a.2.].

c. Colorimeters may produce a matching mixture by subtractive synthesis, in which case they are called *subtractive colorimeters* [5.2.2b.].

d. Colorimeters may use the human visual receptor or a physical receptor as the photoreceptor.

Chapter Seven

Color-Discrimination Measurement

Color discrimination is the perception of differences among colors and is generally specified in terms of thresholds determined by psychophysical methods. The facts of color discrimination provide a working basis for solving many practical color problems (49, 93, 158, 159, 257).

7.1 *Color discrimination* is defined as the awareness or perception of differences among colors.

7.1.1 Color discrimination is not the direct perception of differences among physical stimuli as such.

a. Physical stimuli are not perceived as such in a discrimination situation but serve to activate a physiological mechanism which produces responses (colors) that may be discriminated as different.

7.1.2 Color discrimination is not the sheer perception of several responses (colors) as such but the distinct perception of *differences* among the responses. What is implied is perception of differences among colors rather than perceptions of colors.

7.1.3 Color discrimination may be general in the sense that there may be perception of an overall difference in color.

7.1.4 Color discrimination may be specific in the sense that there may be perception of a difference in hue, saturation, or brightness.

7.1.5 Technical studies on color discrimination in normal vision

[7.1.5]

have been largely concerned with estimates or measurements of the degree or fineness of color discrimination.

a. Measurements of color discrimination are important because they provide indices of the limitations of normal human vision.
b. Measurements of color discrimination reveal considerable differences from one person to another in the capacity to discriminate colors.
c. Measurements of color discrimination indicate in general that visual discrimination of colors is, under the most favorable conditions, better than the best available physical detector.
d. Measurements of color discrimination afford a working basis for setting up visual standards, viewing conditions, specifications, and color tolerances in relation to a variety of practical problems.

7.2 The basic measure of sensory discrimination is called the *threshold*.

7.2.1 A *discrimination threshold* is expressed generally as a relation between a change in stimulus and a difference in response, as follows:

$$\Delta R = f(\Delta S)$$

where ΔR represents a discriminable difference in response and ΔS a change in stimulus required for the discrimination.
7.2.2 *Color-discrimination thresholds* may be defined in general in stimulus-response terms, as follows:

$$\Delta R = f(\Delta X, \Delta Y, \Delta Z)$$

where ΔR represents a discriminable difference in color (whether overall or specifically in hue, saturation, or brightness), and ΔX, ΔY, and ΔZ represent the change in the stimulus required for the discrimination.

a. CIE tristimulus values are associated with stimulus dimensions and may be conveniently used to specify color-discrimination thresholds.

7.2.3 Although color-discrimination thresholds are properly described as *hue, saturation,* and *brightness thresholds*, they are conveniently specified in CIE terms.

[7.2]

7.2.4 Thresholds, in general, may be classified as *differential* and *absolute.*

a. The *differential color threshold* may be defined as the difference in λ_D, P_e, and Y (or x, y, and Y) associated with two colors that can be discriminated in 50 percent of numerous trials. The term *differential hue* (or *saturation,* or *brightness*) *threshold* is used when a single color dimension is being studied.

b. The *absolute color threshold* is a special case of a differential threshold.

1. The *absolute brightness threshold* is a limiting case of the differential brightness threshold and may be defined, for a given chromaticity, as the minimal change in luminance required for perception of a difference in brightness from a background of zero luminance in 50 percent of numerous trials.

2. The *absolute saturation threshold* is a limiting case of the differential saturation threshold and may be defined as the minimal change in purity at some λ_D required for perception of a difference in saturation from a neutral background of fixed luminance in 50 percent of numerous trials.

7.3 *Psychophysical methods* are used in determining thresholds and, for threshold determinations, can be classified into three principal types (with variations on them).

7.3.1 The *matching method* (*method of adjustment, average error, reproduction*) is the psychophysical method in which the observer adjusts a variable, or test stimulus, until the color response it produces matches the response to a standard stimulus.

a. Variation of a test stimulus in color matching usually involves all three dimensions of color at once (as with a colorimeter), but there may be variation along a single color-stimulus dimension that can be represented along some single vector in CIE space, such as a line of constant λ_D.

b. When one-dimensional variation in color is used in threshold measurements, the statistical measure usually employed in the matching method is the mean (specification) of a number of

[7.3.1]

matches for the absolute threshold, and the standard deviation for the differential threshold.

c. Where continuous three-dimensional variation in color is used in threshold measurements, as with a colorimeter, special multidimensional statistics must be employed in handling the data (106, 268, 269).

d. The matching method is the easiest and most adaptable of the psychophysical methods and has been used extensively in color-discrimination studies.

7.3.2 The *method of limits* (*minimal change, serial exploration*) is the psychophysical method in which the experimenter repeatedly varies the test stimulus upwards and/or downwards in small steps, and the observer signals the relation between his response to the test stimulus and his response to the criterion (greater than, less than, or equal to for differential thresholds, and the presence or absence of sensation for absolute thresholds).

a. The method of limits is most typically used where the color-stimulus variation has only one degree of freedom.

b. The statistical measure usually employed in the method of limits is the mean (specification) of the test stimulus at the transition points.

7.3.3 The *method of constant stimuli* is the psychophysical method in which test stimuli that bracket the criterion (either the absolute threshold or a fixed standard) are presented repeatedly in random order and the observer signals, for each test stimulus, the relation between his response to the test stimulus and his response to the criterion.

a. The method of constant stimuli is most typically used where the color-stimulus variation has only one degree of freedom.

b. The statistical measure usually employed in the method of constant stimuli is the 50 percent point on the psychometric function produced from many repetitions of the stimulus series.

c. When the method of constant stimuli is used for determining the differential threshold, it is usually called the method of *constant stimulus differences.*

7.4. Color discrimination can be expressed in terms of the three color-response dimensions (hue, saturation, and brightness) or ex-

[7.4]

pressed as psychophysical specifications respectively of dominant wavelength, purity, (or chromaticity coordinates) and luminance.

7.4.1 Absolute threshold values for each of the three color dimensions serve as one means of expressing color sensitivity.

a. The *absolute brightness threshold* represents least perceptible brightness.

1. Under optimal conditions, the absolute brightness threshold may correspond to a luminance level of about 0.001 to 0.005 foot-lambert for foveal cones and 0.000001 foot-lambert for rods.

2. Full cone vision does not come into use until a luminance level of about 0.1 foot-lambert is reached.

b. The *photochromatic threshold,* defined as the lowest luminance at which hue is perceived, is nearly identical with the absolute brightness threshold from the extreme long-wave end of the spectrum down to a wavelength of about 620 mμ, but below this point the photochromatic threshold rises to a much higher level than the absolute brightness threshold for rods [3.1.1c.] [Fig. 7.1] (56, 229).

c. The *absolute saturation threshold* represents least perceptible saturation and may be obtained when a spectrally selective stimulus is additively mixed with a non-selective stimulus.

1. The absolute saturation threshold varies as a function of wavelength, with a sharp maximum at about 570 mμ and a rapid drop to 0.1 (or less) of the maximum value below 450 and above 650 mμ [Fig. 7.2] (182, 206, 228).

2. The absolute saturation threshold varies inversely with luminance up to about 100 foot-lamberts.

7.4.2 *Differential threshold* values for each of the color dimensions serve as a second means of expressing *color sensitivity.*

a. The *differential brightness threshold* represents a just-perceptible difference in brightness and is usually expressed as the ratio: $\Delta Y/Y$.

1. Over an extended range of luminance (about 1 to 1000 foot-lamberts) at everyday levels, the differential brightness threshold is practically constant, but the threshold increases

[7.4.2a.1.]

markedly at low luminance levels and slightly at very high levels [Fig. 7.3].

a) At low luminance levels a difference in luminance of 20 to 30 percent or more between an object and its background may be required before the object is discriminated.

b) With optimal conditions, i.e., a very large test field, a sharp dividing line between the two halves of the field, high luminance, and a well-adapted eye, the differential brightness threshold ($\Delta Y/Y$) can be as low as 0.005 (23, 117, 258).

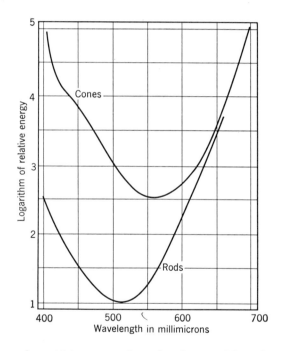

Fig. 7.1   Spectral sensitivity curves for rod and cone vision, showing the relative energy required to produce a threshold response.   The actual energy increment above the threshold for the appearance of color (cone function) varies for different parts of the retina.   In the parafovea it is between 0.1 and 1.0 log unit.   The distance between the two curves represents the photochromatic interval.   (Hecht and Hsia, 1945.)   From Stevens, S. S. (Ed.), *Handbook of Experimental Psychology*, New York: John Wiley & Sons, Inc., 1951, Fig. 24, p. 950.

[7.4.2]

c) Under customary experimental conditions of a dark surround and a bipartite test area of only a few degrees, the differential brightness threshold ($\Delta Y/Y$) is about 0.02 to 0.03.

b. What is referred to as the *differential hue threshold* generally represents a just-perceptible difference in color for stimuli at constant colorimetric purity and luminance, and it is usually expressed as the difference in millimicrons between the two wavelengths associated with the differentiated colors ($\Delta\lambda_D$).

1. For spectral stimuli in a small test field ($2°$) with an average retinal illumination of 70 trolands, the differential hue

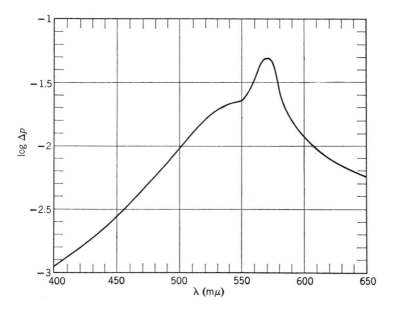

Fig. 7.2 Absolute saturation threshold according to Priest and Brickwedde. Photometric field of $4°$ viewed through a 3 mm artificial pupil, and a retinal illumination of about 80 trolands, the field having an extensive surround of 10 trolands. Color temperature of the white light about 5000°K. Monochromatic luminance measured by a flicker method; method of limits; two observers. From LeGrand, Yves, *Light, Colour and Vision*, Fig. 74, p. 276. (Translated by R. W. G. Hunt, J. W. T. Walsh, and F. R. W. Hunt, New York: John Wiley & Sons, Inc., 1957.)

[7.4.2b.1.]

threshold is about 1 to 2 mμ (by the method of limits) for most of the visible spectrum, but it is several times this value at the extreme ends of the light spectrum [Fig. 7.4] (155, 294).

a) Two significant minima are generally reported in the hue-discrimination curve for spectral stimuli, one at about 590 mμ and the other at about 490 mμ.

1) At about 490 mμ and also at 590 mμ, the eye detects a hue difference for the least change in wavelength.
2) The minimum at 590 mμ in the hue-discrimination curve may be as low as 1 mμ.

b) In the hue-discrimination curve, there are found other minimum points which are higher than those at 490 mμ and 590 mμ; the most commonly reported is at about 440 mμ.
c) As a function of colorimetric purity, what is referred to as the differential hue threshold falls rapidly once the absolute saturation threshold has been passed, and has a mini-

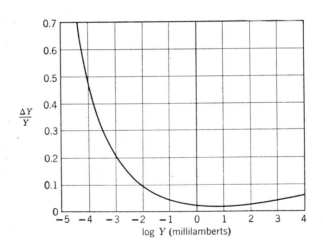

Fig. 7.3   Brightness discrimination curve: $\dfrac{\Delta Y}{Y}$ plotted against Y, where ΔY represents the just noticeable brightness difference at luminance B.   From Wright, W. D., *Researches on Normal and Defective Colour Vision*, St. Louis: The C. V. Mosby Co., 1947, Fig. 26, p. 26.

[7.4.2b.1.]

mum at purities between 0.1 and 0.2 for λ_D less than 490 mμ but at unity for λ_D greater than 490 mμ (273).

d) For a 2° field and retinal illuminance of about 70 trolands, it has been found that about 150 hues can be distinguished in the responses to single-frequency bands of the light spectrum.

1) With a test field larger than 2°, it is expected that many more than 150 discriminable hues could be found in responses to single-frequency bands of the light spectrum (185).

e) Little is known with regard to hue discrimination for the fovea at very high and very low luminances, for the periphery of the retina at all luminances, and for fields larger than 2°.

c. The *differential saturation threshold* represents a just-perceptible difference in saturation and is usually expressed as the

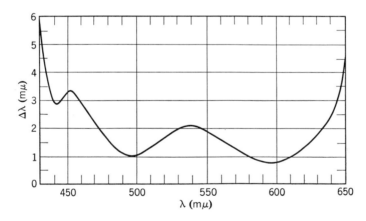

Fig. 7.4 Differential color sensitivity throughout the spectrum, according to Wright and Pitt. Wright's colorimeter, free from diffused light, 2° field, average retinal illumination 70 trolands except in the extreme blue, method of limits. From LeGrand, Yves, *Light, Colour and Vision*, Fig. 73, p. 275. (Translated by R. W. G. Hunt, J. W. T. Walsh, and F. R. W. Hunt, New York: John Wiley & Sons, Inc., 1957.)

[7.4.2c.]

change in purity required for discrimination of the difference (ΔP_c).

1. As purity is varied from 0 to 1.0, the differential saturation threshold reaches a maximum at some intermediate purity for most hues [Fig. 7.5].

2. Saturation may be measured as the number of just-noticeable saturation steps between neutral and any wavelength region in the spectrum; the smallest number of steps is found at about 570 mμ [Fig. 7.6].

a) The color responses aroused by light of long or short wavelengths are highly saturated relative to those aroused by light of wavelengths at about 570 mμ, and many more discriminable saturation steps are found at the long and short wavelengths.

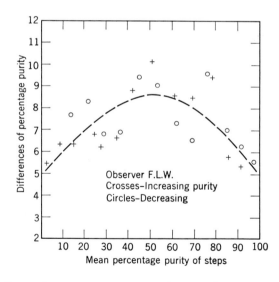

Fig. 7.5 Differential saturation sensitivity (expressed in terms of purity) at various purity values between neutral (4800°K) and the spectral radiation of wavelength 0.65μ. (Light adapted eyes.) From Wright, W. D., *Researches on Normal and Defective Colour Vision*, St. Louis: The C. V. Mosby Co., 1947, Fig. 91, p. 163.

[7.4]

7.5 The *color-discrimination solid* is a three-dimensional figure which can be used to represent all discriminable color differences.

7.5.1 Since color has three dimensions, color discrimination can be represented by distances in a three-dimensional space (not necessarily Euclidean space) in which the dimensions correspond to the three color dimensions.

a. The vertical axis of the color-discrimination solid represents increasing brightness upward.
b. Lines radiating horizontally outward from the vertical axis of the color-discrimination solid represent increasing saturation.

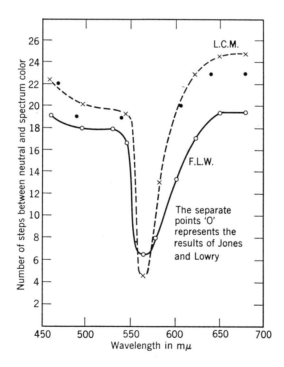

Fig. 7.6 Number of just-perceptible steps between neutral (color temperature 4800°K) and the colors produced by the spectrum in a 2° field for two observers (FLW and LCM). From Wright, W. D., *Researches on Normal and Defective Colour Vision,* St. Louis: The C. V. Mosby Co., 1947, Fig. 89, p. 162.

[7.5.1]

c. Distances along circumferential lines or angles around the vertical axis of the color-discrimination solid represent hue.

d. An estimate of the number of perceptible steps in a color-discrimination solid for surfaces, calibrated in visually uniform Munsell intervals, shows there are about 7,500,000 colors that may be discriminated under the best observational conditions (207).

e. A color-discrimination solid for emitted light would be larger than that for reflected light because of the greater ranges of luminance and purity available in the former; the total number of detectably different colors has been estimated at 10,000,000 or more (159).

7.5.2 *Overall color differences* may be estimated in a color-discrimination solid by the length of a vector connecting two color locations in the three-dimensional space, if the scales have been adjusted to approximately equal visual intervals. It is not known whether such an adjustment is strictly possible in an Euclidean space, but a good approximation may be possible.

a. Attempts have been made to estimate overall color differences using equations based on characteristics of the color-discrimination solid.

b. One practical, useful equation for estimating overall color difference in Munsell terms is called the *Godlove small-color-difference formula,* named after the author who reported it. The Godlove formula is as follows:

$$G = [2C_1 C_2 \emptyset H + (\Delta C)^2 + (4\,\Delta V)^2]^{\frac{1}{2}}$$

where $\emptyset H = (1 - \cos 3.6° \,\Delta H)$
and G = Godlove units of color difference.
C_1 and C_2 = the chromas of the two samples.
ΔC = difference in the chromas of the two samples.
ΔV = difference in the values of the two samples.
ΔH = difference in the hues of the two samples.

H, V, and C are all expressed in Munsell units.

c. There are many other color-difference formulas (159), all of which are valid only to the extent that the spatial models on which they are based are valid representations of uniform color space.

Chapter Eight

Object-Color Systems

Systems of object-color samples are organized according to colorant characteristics, according to color-stimulus syntheses, or according to color responses, and uses of the systems vary depending on the basic plan of organization (159).

8.1 Systems of *object-color standards* include chips or samples that cover a considerable range of object-colors, so that for any object chosen at random within the range a fairly close duplicate can be found in the set. These organized systems of material standards are called *object-color systems* and may serve as a form of color specification.

8.2 Material object-color standards are convenient and so are often used in commerce in preference to specification according to the CIE system [6.3.2].

8.3 There are three general plans used for the internal construction of systematic collections of object-color standards; one is based on characteristics of colorants, one on color-stimulus syntheses, and one on color responses.

> **8.3.1** One general plan for constructing systems of object-color standards is called the *colorant-mixture plan,* since it is based on the systematic mixture of pigments or dyes [5.2.2d.].

[8.3.1]

a. In the development of an object-color system according to to the colorant-mixture plan, a limited number of dyes or pigments is used to develop the object-color gamut through mixture of these materials in systematically varied proportions.
b. Understanding a colorant-mixture system requires a knowledge of the particular mixture plan by which it was developed.
c. One of the more complete colorant-mixture systems used in American industry is the *Martin-Senour Nu-Hue Custom Color System.*

1. The Nu-Hue system was developed from eight basic paints: six chromatic, one near-black, and one white.
2. The Nu-Hue system contains 1000 painted cards, mat finish, available in two forms: 3″ x 5″ cards in a plastic case, or disks mounted in systematic array between transparent cover plates.
3. The 1000 cards in the Nu-Hue system illustrate the range of the object-colors producible by eight basic paints, including near-black and white.
4. For each of the 1000 cards in the Nu-Hue system, the amounts by weight and volume of the eight base paints are known; it is possible by measuring out these amounts to mix a satisfactory match for any of the cards shown.
5. The base-paints in the Nu-Hue system were chosen for permanence, with some restriction in gamut for red-purple to blue as a result.
6. The Nu-Hue system includes paints commonly used for decorating houses outside and in and has been very successful in promoting the sale of prescription-mixed paint.

d.   Other colorant mixture systems found in general use are: *The Colorizer, Plochere Color System, Nu-Hue Color Coordinator.*

8.3.2 A second general plan for constructing systems of object-color standards is called the *stimulus-synthesis* (or CSS) *plan,* since it is based on systematic stimulus combinations [5.2.2].

a. In the development of a color-order system according to the CSS plan, the light from a limited number of object-color samples is used to develop the full object-color gamut through com-

[8.3.2]

bination of the light in systematically varied proportions; material standards are then made to show the sequences of object colors produced in this manner.

b. Understanding a CSS system requires a knowledge of the particular CSS plan by which it was developed.

c. Additive CSS is the basis for the fundamental CIE standard coordinate system of colorimetry, and object-color standards related to systematic variations in CSS are readily translated into units of the standard system.

d. Object-color sequences obtained by CSS simulate, in many instances, familiar sequences found in everyday life.

e. Object-color sequences obtained by averaging CSS approximate those obtainable in chromatic printing by the frequently used halftone screen process.

f. One of the more complete averaging CSS systems used in American industry is the *Container Corporation Color Harmony Manual*.

1. The *Color Harmony Manual* (3rd edition) was based on the German *Ostwald* system [Fig. 8.1] and developed from 30 object colors of different dominant wavelength and maximum obtainable purity (14 pairs of complementaries and 2 intermediates), and a 9-step gray scale. All intermediate chips for each dominant-wavelength chart were produced by colorant mixture to match systematic variations in excitation purity and luminance [6.3.3c.1.c)].

2. The *Color Harmony Manual* (3rd edition) contains 943 individual removable chips, mat finish on one side, glossy finish on the other, mounted systematically on heavy loose-leaf pages in a carrying case.

3. The 943 chips in the *Color Harmony Manual* (3rd edition) illustrate the systematic sequences that may be achieved by averaging CSS.

4. For each of the chips in the first three editions of the *Color Harmony Manual* the colorimetric specifications for illumination by daylight are known for the mat side (and for the glossy side of the 3rd edition); it is possible, therefore, to interpolate between the known specifications of adjacent samples and obtain a moderately accurate specification for an unknown sample bounded by certain samples (79, 97, 98).

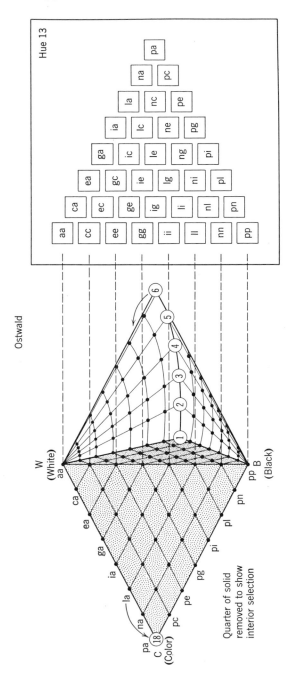

Fig. 8-1.   Ostwald Color System.   A system describing object-colors in terms of Color Content, White Content, and Black Content, usually exemplified by charts in triangular form with Full Color, White and Black at the apices, providing a gray scale of White and Black mixtures and parallel scales of constant White Content and constant Black Content as these grays are mixed with varying proportions of the Full Color for each of 24 or more triangles to form a collection of charts.   Samples on each chart illustrate constant dominant wavelength (called hue), with samples lying parallel to the gray scale constant in purity (called Shadow Series).   See diagram.   From ISCC *Newsletter*, No. 156; Nov.–Dec., 1961.   D. Nickerson.

[8.3.2f.]

5. The pigments used in the *Color Harmony Manual* were chosen for maximum permanence and were applied to a transparent cellulose acetate base of highly stable characteristics.
6. The *Color Harmony Manual* has been used as an analytical approach to color harmony and in the specification of object-colors.

g. Another averaging CSS system often referred to in the earlier literature is *Ridgeway's Color Standards and Color Nomenclature.*

8.3.3 A third general plan for constructing systems of object-color standards is called the *appearance plan,* defined as one having scales which depend on the judgment of color intervals.

a. In the development of an object-color system according to the appearance plan, an attempt is made to sample colors with a collection of chips producing responses that may be ordered into uniformly graded series of hue, saturation, and brightness, to represent the perceptual dimensions of color [1.3.5a.].

1. The intervals between chips in an appearance system are determined by human observers who make many judgments regarding the size of the intervals; the final set of chips is adjusted so that the intervals conform to the judgments.
2. Judgments of object-color intervals must always be made under a standard set of viewing conditions; the intervals may hold only for that set of conditions.

b. Understanding an appearance system requires a knowledge of the particular procedure by which it was developed.
c. One of the more complete appearance systems used in American industry is the *Munsell Color System* [Fig. 8.2], which is exemplified by the object-color samples included in the *Munsell Book of Color.*

1. The Munsell Color System was developed from judgments of equal hue, value (brightness), and chroma (saturation) and includes 40 equally spaced hues on a scale from 0–100, a value scale of 10 equally spaced brightness intervals, and absolute chroma scales (number of steps depending on hue and value)

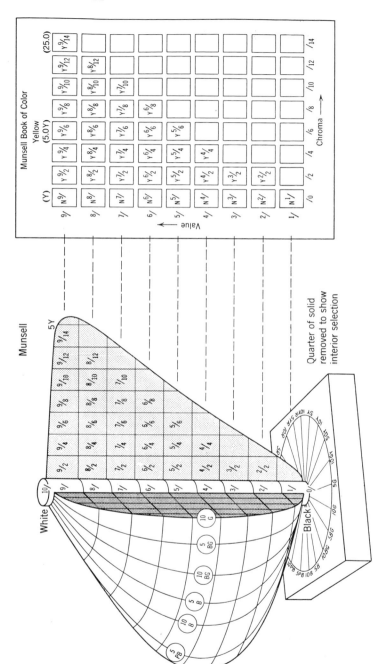

Fig. 8.2   Munsell Color System.   A system of specifying object-colors on scales of hue, value, and chroma, exemplified by a collection of chips forming an atlas of charts that show scales for which two of the three variables are constant, the hue scales containing five principal and five intermediate hues, the value scale containing ten steps from black to white, and the chroma scales showing up to 16 steps from the equivalent gray.   All three scales are intended to represent equal visual (not physical) intervals for a normal observer and daylight viewing with gray to white surroundings.   From ISCC *Newsletter*, No. 156, Nov–Dec., 1961.   D. Nickerson.

representing equal differences in saturation [6.4.2c.] (198, 205).

2. The *Munsell Book of Color* contains over 1200 individually removable chips, in either glossy or mat finish, in a two-volume loose-leaf cabinet edition. It is also available in loose-leaf pocket editions and in various briefer forms for special purposes.

3. The chips in the *Munsell Book of Color* illustrate the systematic sequences that are found in equal visual intervals of color, regardless of the variations required in the physical stimulus to produce them.

4. Colorimetric specifications are known for all of the chips in the *Munsell Book of Color* for illumination by daylight, and about half the chips have been specified for eight other illuminants including tungsten and various fluorescent illuminants. It is possible, therefore, to interpolate between the known specifications of adjacent samples and obtain a moderately accurate specification for an unknown sample bounded by certain samples (208).

5. The pigments used in the *Munsell Book of Color* were chosen for permanence, and the colorants used in each sample are applied within very strict tolerances to a white paper base.

6. The Munsell Color System has been used for teaching color spacing, as an analytical approach to color harmony, and in the specification of object colors.

7. The Munsell Color System provides a nearly uniform-interval basis for color appearance measurement, provided average daylight, either natural or artificial, is used as the illuminant.

8.3.4 Some systems of object-color standards combine characteristics of the general plans, and may be said to use, therefore, an *intermediate plan*.

a. When object-color standards are produced by systematic screening variations in the screen-plate printing process, an intermediate plan is used.

1. In the screen-plate process of printing the final results are obtained by spatial-averaging CSS [5.2.2a.2.], but where the printed dots overlap, the color produced by each dot corresponds to colorant mixture or subtractive CSS [5.2.2b.].

[8.3.4]

b. Progressive amounts of coverage with a single colorant by the screen-plate printing process produce a series of colors ranging from the white produced by the paper to the color produced by the ink, printed solid; this series corresponds to spatial-averaging CSS by juxtaposition of small dots unresolved by the eye [5.2.2a.2.].

c. In the screen-plate printing process, when a second colorant series is printed over the first colorant series, a mixture of the two colorants and the white of the paper is produced; the over-lapped dots produce subtractive CSS or colorant mixture, and the visual synthesis of the reflected light from these dots with the light reflected from the paper between the dots constitutes spatial-averaging CSS.

d. Some of the most valuable object-color charts are produced by printing; reference samples which have sufficient uniformity and permanence to be of practical value are provided at reasonable cost.

e. One of the more complete intermediate systems used in American industry is the *Maerz and Paul, A Dictionary of Color.*

> **1.** The Maerz and Paul dictionary contains 7056 different object-color samples printed on semi-gloss paper, 6048 of which are $\frac{1}{2}''$ x $\frac{5}{8}''$ rectangles, and 1008 of the darker of which are $1\frac{1}{16}''$ x $\frac{5}{8}''$ rectangles.
>
> **2.** The Maerz and Paul dictionary was produced from eight chromatic and seven base gray pigments, and the mixtures were accomplished by halftone screen printing.
>
> **3.** In the Maerz and Paul dictionary, the hue circle is covered in eight intervals—bR to R, R to YR, YR to Y, Y to G, G to BG, BG to B, B to BR, and BR to bR; each hue interval is represented by a series of eight charts.
>
> **4.** Two printing impressions are used to produce the charts in the Maerz and Paul dictionary, resulting in variations in hue, saturation, and brightness.
>
> **5.** The Maerz and Paul dictionary contains an alphabetical list of 4000 color names, with a key to the location of the corresponding samples in the charts; the object-color samples in the charts are identified by these names.
>
> **6.** The large number of samples in the Maerz and Paul dic-

[8.3.4e.]

tionary makes the steps between successive samples so small that interpolation is often not necessary.

7. The Maerz and Paul dictionary may be used as a collection of practical object-color standards in almost any area where such standards are required.

8.3.5 At least one prominent system of object-color standards, the *Villalobos Colour Atlas,* has combined characteristics of all three general plans for generating a systematic collection of object-color samples.

a. The *Villalobos Colour Atlas* was produced from multiple impressions with a halftone screening process, and with only screening intervals that produced constant hue planes and uniformly spaced hue and brightness (but not saturation) intervals.

b. The *Villalobos Colour Atlas* contains 7279 object-color samples, 1 cm square, with a 4-mm hole cut out of each to facilitate comparisons.

c. The *Villalobos Colour Atlas* was printed from 38 base chromatic inks to give glossy samples adjusted so that the hue intervals produced are approximately equal, and the colors produced by inks 19 hue steps apart are intended to be colorimetric complementaries.

d. Each object-color series in the *Villalobos Colour Atlas* is achieved by bulk mixture of printing ink, precisely controlled to produce constant hue.

e. The *Villalobos Colour Atlas* includes a gray scale ranging from black to white in 20 steps in which the increments are adjusted for visual equality.

f. For each of the 38 base chromatic inks in the *Villalobos Colour Atlas,* 19 series of samples are shown, each sample in the series having closely the same daylight reflectance as the corresponding gray.

g. Each chip in the *Villalobos Colour Atlas* is identified by a hue letter, a brightness value, and a number indicating degree of chromaticity. Degrees of chromaticity represent saturation steps, and the steps are uniform for a given hue and brightness value, but step size varies from one hue and brightness value to another.

[8.3.5]

h. The large number of samples, the wide object-color gamut, and the excellent uniformity of spacing in the *Villalobos Colour Atlas* make it possible to find a color match for any unknown uniform surface, so that interpolation is seldom necessary.

8.4 Object-color *sequences* will vary from one object-color system to another, even within those organized according to the same basic plan, and the sequences will vary importantly among systems developed according to different general plans.

8.5 *Spacing* of object-color sequences will vary from one object-color system to another even within those organized according to the same basic plan, and the spacing will vary importantly among systems developed according to different general plans.

8.6 There are many non-systematic collections of object-color samples designed for special purposes as an aid in the specification and grading of samples common to specialized fields of art and commerce. Included among these collections are standards for fabrics, plastics, glass, fibers, paint, printing inks, architectural materials, soils, ceramics, fruits, flowers, vegetables, electrical wiring, plumbing, petroleum, vegetable oils, animal tallows, and greases.

8.7 Selection of an object-color system for efficient use in any particular application requires specific knowledge not only of the general plan but of the specific procedures used in developing the system and of the sequences and spacing of sequences within the system. The pitfalls are many for the unwary user of object-color systems.

Chapter Nine

Color Names—A Form of Color Specification

Colors are systematically named according to their visual attributes of hue, saturation, and brightness. Systematically organized color names may serve as a useful though imprecise form of color specification (167).

9.1 The color vocabularies used in diverse fields of art, science, and industry are in some cases similar, but the vocabulary used in one field is frequently unintelligible to workers in a different field.

9.2 The Inter-Society Color Council, National Bureau of Standards (ISCC-NBS) *Method of Designating Colors and a Dictionary of Color Names* (National Bureau of Standards Circular 553, 1955) was compiled as a record of the approximate visual specifications of 7500 individual color names, to make it possible to translate from one color vocabulary to another, and to relate color names to the Munsell Color System [8.3.3c.].

9.3 Color names typically used in art, science, and industry are translated in the ISCC-NBS system into simple descriptive hue designations with appropriate modifiers that indicate saturation and brightness [Fig. 9.1].

[9.3]

9.4 The ISCC-NBS system of color names is defined by 38 charts, within which color names are designated for appropriate ranges of variation in the Munsell notation; there are 267 such ranges or "blocks" [Fig. 9.2].

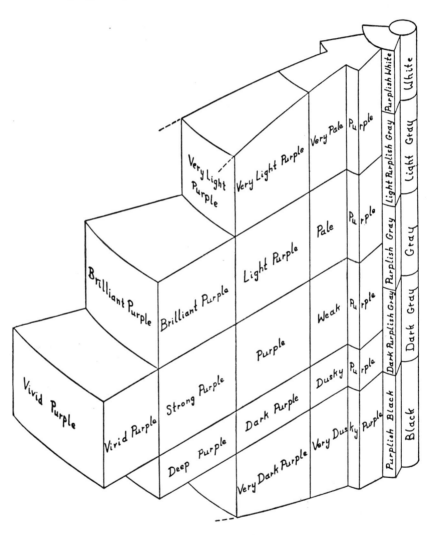

Fig. 9.1 Illustration of the tridimensional nature of the definitions of the ISCC-NBS color designations. From Judd, D. B., *Color in Business, Science, and Industry*, New York: John Wiley & Sons, Inc., 1952, Fig. 91, p. 294.

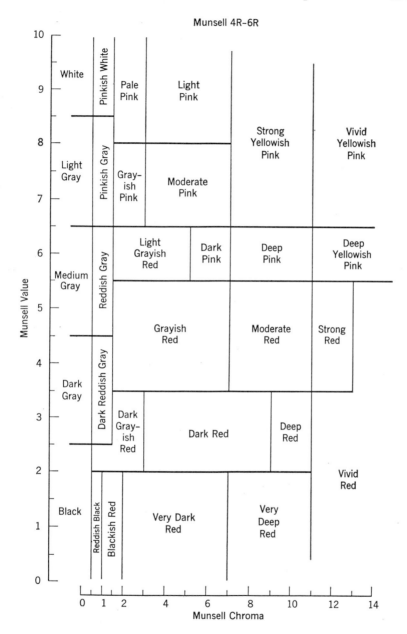

Fig. 9.2   The Inter-Society Color Council–National Bureau of Standards (ISCC-NBS) method of designation in conjunction with the Munsell notation.   From Judd, D. B., *Color in Business, Science, and Industry,* New York: John Wiley & Sons, Inc., 1952, Fig. 92.

[9.4]

9.4.1 The charts of the ISCC-NBS system of color names make use of 17 hue designations, 5 value designations, 3 chroma designations, and 6 designations for variations in value and chroma together, combined to produce a total of 267 designations.

9.4.2 Some value and chroma designations in the ISCC-NBS system of color names are different depending on whether they refer to opaque or clear materials.

9.4.3 Standard color names in the ISCC-NBS system may be obtained from CIE specifications, derived from spectrophotometric or colorimetric measurements, or related to color names found in commercially published lists.

9.5 The ISCC-NBS system of color names has been used to correlate the 7500 color names found in 14 recognized systems of color nomenclature. In NBS Circular 553 all color names for each of the 267 ISCC-NBS color designations have been listed together.

9.6 One section of NBS Circular 553, dealing with the ISCC-NBS system of color names, is a dictionary proper that includes an alphabetical list of 7500 color names with their corresponding ISCC-NBS color designations.

9.7 The color names of the ISCC-NBS system of color names are related to Munsell notations for conditions where average daylight (CIE Source C) is used to illuminate the sample at 45°, the sample is viewed perpendicular to its surface, and a neutral gray surround is used.

Section III

Marginal Facts

Chapter Ten

Color-Vision Theory

When a color stimulus acts on the color receptors, what happens in the receptors and their attached nerves is so poorly understood that it is still only possible to speculate about how color responses are produced (92, 93, 138, 159, 212).

10.1 A systematic attempt to explain how color responses are produced is called a *theory of color vision.*

10.1.1 A particular theory of color vision comprises a set of deductions designed to explain how color stimuli acting on the visual receptors can produce the color responses that have been recorded in experiments on color vision or observed in everyday life.

10.1.2 Theories of color vision are not facts, as such, but repre-sent attempts to integrate the established facts of color vision.

10.1.3 Theories of color vision typically attempt to deduce physiological models or mechanisms that would account for the facts of color vision and so predict physiological facts that (often) still need to be established.

10.1.4 There are many theories of color vision, yet no one theory has been able to account rigorously for all the established facts of color vision. Some theories have, however, been more successful than others.

10.1.5 A fully acceptable theory of color vision must explain all the well-established facts of color vision.

[10.1.5]

a. Theories of color vision must explain such things as the color-mixture functions; various forms of color-vision defect; the photopic and scotopic luminosity functions; the facts of chromatic adaptation and the related facts of color constancy; the unitary perceptual nature of red, yellow, green, and blue; the Bezold-Brücke effect; after-images; hue, saturation, and brightness discrimination; spatial and temporal effects; invariant hues; binocular interactions; and others [3, 4].

10.1.6 Basic to all theories of color vision are certain well-accepted physiological facts.

a. Within the retina are the immediate organs of vision, the visual receptors.
b. The visual receptors respond by initiating neural activity which is propagated to the optic nerve and higher nerve centers.
c. The visual receptors for scotopic vision are the retinal rods.
d. The rods' response is due to a photochemical substance called rhodopsin.
e. The visual receptors for photopic vision are usually considered to be the retinal cones.

10.1.7 Certain significant facts on which color-vision theories depend remain to be experimentally established.

a. The nature of the mechanism that gives the cones their spectral sensitivities is still largely a matter of conjecture.
b. The combinations of cone responses that result in activity in the optic nerve are still matters of conjecture.
c. Interactions within the visual paths of the nervous system are still a matter of conjecture.

10.2 The oldest, most parsimonious, and most persistent theory of color vision is known as the *Young-Helmholtz three-component theory* of color vision.

10.2.1 The Young-Helmholtz theory has a *stimulus basis* and derives from the fact that any color can be represented by a unique mixture of three differently colored lights.
10.2.2 The Young-Helmholtz theory assumes parsimoniously that there are *three kinds of receptors* in the eyes that react selectively to light according to its wavelength.

[10.2]

10.2.3 Each of the three kinds of receptors required by the Young-Helmholtz theory is connected to its own set of nerves, and each sends on its own special message.

10.2.4 According to the Young-Helmholtz theory, the messages from the three kinds of receptors are combined in the visual system at the moment colors are seen.

10.2.5 According to the Young-Helmholtz theory, the particular color seen depends on which receptors are acted on by light and how much they respond to the light.

10.2.6 The Young-Helmholtz theory has several defects that have been pointed out from time to time.

> **a.** The Young-Helmholtz theory does not provide ready explanation for the existence of the unitary perceptions: red, yellow, green, and blue; in particular, the unitary nature of yellow is not satisfactorily explained [3.1.2a.2.].
>
> **b.** The Young-Helmholtz theory does not account for the changes in perceived hue that take place with a change in intensity of the stimulus (Bezold-Brücke effect) [3.1.1e.].
>
> **c.** The Young-Helmholtz theory has many forms, depending on the choice of primary color stimuli, no one of which approaches the explanatory power of all; for example, the primaries best suited to an account of the effects of chromatic adaptation do not accord with giving a maximally straightforward account of the various types of color blindness, and vice versa.

10.3 A second and somewhat complex theory of color vision is known as the *Hering opponent-colors theory.*

10.3.1 The Hering theory has a *response basis,* and it derives from the assumption that there are six basic unitary colors (red, yellow, green, blue, white, and black), no one of which partakes of any other [3.1.2a.].

10.3.2 The Hering theory assumes that light is absorbed in the receptors by light-sensitive chemicals, that this absorption starts activity in the rest of the visual system, and that this activity is directly responsible for the colors we see.

10.3.3 According to the Hering theory, activity in the visual system (responsible for six basic color qualities) is not found in six

[10.3.3]

separate systems but in *three* pairs of processes, with the two members of each pair being opposites or *opponent processes*.

a. According to the Hering theory, there is a blue-yellow pair of processes in the visual system in which "blue" events are *opponent* or antagonistic to "yellow" events, so that a particular color may look either bluish or yellowish but never both at the same time, i.e., blue cancels yellow, and yellow, blue.

b. According to the Hering theory, there is a green-red pair of processes in the visual system in which "green" events are *opponent* or antagonistic to "red" events, so that a particular color may look either greenish or reddish but never both at the same time, i.e., red cancels green, and green, red.

c. According to the Hering theory, there is a white-black pair of processes in the visual system in which "white" events are opponent to "black" events, in the sense that a particular color may depart from a middle gray toward white or black but never toward both at the same time, i.e., white does not cancel black but blends with it to produce gray.

10.3.4 According to the Hering theory, the particular color seen depends on which of the three opponent processes are responding, the (opponent) directions of the responses, and the amounts of the responses.

10.3.5 The Hering theory has several defects, which have been pointed out from time to time.

a. The Hering theory predicts a form of yellow-blue blindness (tetartanopia), no uncomplicated case of which has ever been reported.

b. The Hering theory fails to predict two (protanopia and tritanopia) of the three chief types of dichromatism and accounts for them as variations of deuteranopia and tetartanopia, respectively, only by an ad hoc assumption which admits an unlimited series of such variations.

c. In the Hering theory, no one set of values for the "constants" connecting the photochemical stage with the nerve fiber stage serves nearly as well as the use of a different set for each phenomenon.

d. Since the concepts of "white" and "black" (assumed as unitary responses in the Hering theory) are not simply brightness

[10.3]

terms but relate to lightness, it has been argued that the Hering theory does not provide for the perception of brightness as opposed to lightness.

10.4   There have been many variations and additions to the Young-Helmholtz and the Hering theories of color vision, and these two theories provide the jumping-off place for most other theories; both theories recognize that a set of *three* functions is *necessary* and *sufficient* for the treatment of the facts of color vision [Table 10.1].

10.4.1   A number of theories of color vision have been offered which recognize that a set of three functions is necessary and which incorporate aspects of the Young-Helmholtz theory or the opponent-mechanism concept of Hering or derivative combinations, but they are often concerned with explaining the phenomena of brightness perception as distinct from the processes by which chromatic perceptions are mediated.   Some of these theories assume more than three photosensitive elements (28, 95, 96, 134, 135, 136, 137, 176, 177, 259, 260, 261).

10.4.2   Some theories of color vision are called zone or stage theories and combine aspects of both the Young-Helmholtz and Hering theories.

a. All zone or stage theories require more than one level of physiological activity in the visual mechanism.

b. Zone or stage theories give separate accounts of physiological processes at various levels of the visual mechanism.

c. Theories by von Kries, Schrödinger, Adams, and Müller are examples of complex stage theories which use the Hering opponent-process notion in the description of the final stage or level of activity in the nervous system (2, 92, 158, 170, 191, 241).

10.5   A recent quantified version of the Hering theory, called the *Hurvich-Jameson quantitative opponent-colors theory*, has been successfully used for the quantitative account of more recorded facts of color vision than any theory heretofore explored, and requires only the two stages specified by Hering.

10.5.1   The Hurvich-Jameson theory is a quantitative expression of the Hering theory, since the response functions required by the

Table 10.1 Summary of a Few of the Better-Known Visual Theories

Name	Anatomical Location	Fundamental Colors	Relation to CIE Standard Observer	Chief Limitation
Young, three components	Cone pigments	Red Green Violet	$+3.1956X + 2.4478Y - 0.6434Z$ $-2.5455X + 7.0492Y + 0.4963Z$ $+ 5.0000Z$	Fails to explain dichromatic vision as intended.
Helmholtz, three components	Cone response	Red Green Violet	$+0.070X + 0.945Y - 0.015Z$ $-0.460X + 1.359Y + 0.101Z$ $+ 1.000Z$	Fails to explain color perceptions of protanopes and deuteranopes.
Dominator-modulator, late König	Cone response	Red Green Violet	$+1.000Y$ $-0.460X + 1.359Y + 0.101Z$ $+ 1.000Z$	Fails to explain color perceptions of protanopes and deuteranopes.
Ladd-Franklin, three components, early König	Cone response	Red Green Blue	$+3.7656X + 1.4635Y - 0.2291Z$ $-1.3973X + 6.1289Y + 0.2683Z$ $+ 5.0000Z$	Implies that the blue function has a negative luminosity for normals and deuteranopes, positive for protanopes.
Hering, opponent colors	Optic nerve	Red-green Yellow-blue White-black	$+1.000X - 1.000Y$ $+0.400Y - 0.400Y$ $+1.000Y$	Fails to give an account of protanopia and tritanopia.
Von Kries-Schrödinger, zone or stage	Cone response	Red Green Blue	$+3.7656X + 1.4635Y - 0.2291Z$ $-1.3973X + 6.1289Y + 0.2683Z$ $+ 5.0000Z$	Implies that the blue function has a negative luminosity for normals and deuteranopes, positive for protanopes, fails to give an account of tritanopia.
	Optic nerve	Green-red Blue-yellow White-black	$-3.537X + 3.196Y + 0.341Z$ $+1.341X - 5.884Y + 4.542Z$ $+ 1.000Y$	

Hurvich-Jameson, quantification of Hering opponent colors	Receptor response	α β γ	$-0.3333X + 6.5333Y + 0.1333Z$ $+ 7.0000Y$ $+0.3333X + 6.4667Y - 0.1333Z$	Requires frequency-shift of photosensitive spectral distribution functions to account for protanopia and tritanopia.
	Neural response *	Red-green Yellow-blue White-black	$k_2[1.0000X - 1.0000Y]$ $k_1[0.4000Y - 0.4000Z]$ $(k_3 - k_4)[20.0000Y]$	
Adams, zone or stage	Cone pigments	Red Green Violet	$+3.1956X + 2.4478Y - 0.6434Z$ $-2.5455X + 7.0492Y + 0.4963Z$ $+ 5.0000Z$	Explanations of protanopia and tritanopia based on subsidiary assumptions.
	Cone response *	Red Green Blue	$+1.000X$ $+ 1.000Y$ $+ 1.000Z$	
	Optic nerve *	Red-green Blue-yellow White-black	$+1.000X - 1.000Y$ $- 0.400Y + 0.400Z$ $+ 1.000Y$	
Müller, zone or stage	Cone pigments	Red Green Violet	$+3.1956X + 2.4478Y - 0.6434Z$ $-2.5455X + 7.0492Y + 0.4963Z$ $+ 5.0000Z$	Implausible explanation of protanopic luminosity by resort to luminosity of the yR cone response and luminosity-inhibiting action of the bG cone response, both of which disappear with the yR-bG cone response to produce protanopia.
	Cone response *	yR-bG gY-rB Luminosity	$+5.741X - 4.601Y - 1.140Z$ $-0.932X + 2.750Y - 1.819Z$ $+ 1.000Y$	
	Optic nerve *	Red-green Yellow-blue White-black	$+6.325X - 6.325Y$ $+2.004Y - 2.004Z$ $+ 1.000Y$	

After Judd, D. B., Ch.22 in S. S. Stevens (ed.), Handbook of Experimental Psychology. New York, John Wiley and Sons, Inc., 1951.
* The theory allows for a non-linear dependence of the responses upon the stimulus in addition to the linear dependence indicated here.

[10.5.1]

Hering theory were actually measured experimentally so that a mathematical basis was provided for predicting what colors should be seen under a great variety of conditions.

10.5.2 The Hurvich-Jameson theory assumes an *excitation mechanism* (first stage) in the receptors and an *associated response mechanism* (second stage) elsewhere in the visual system.

a. The *excitation mechanism* of the Hurvich-Jameson theory is assumed to be located in the cones of the retina, and to consist of four light-receiving units containing combinations of *three* photochemicals.

b. The *response mechanism* of the Hurvich-Jameson theory is assumed to be located beyond the retina in the visual nerve centers and to consist of *three* paired opponent-processes: a white-black, a red-green, and a yellow-blue process.

1. The opponent-response processes of the Hurvich-Jameson theory are said to represent *differences* in neural response to stimulation produced by the photochemicals in the excitation mechanism.

c. Spectral distributions for the four primary hue responses (red, yellow, green, and blue) were determined by Hurvich and Jameson by relating the stimulus energy of a narrow band of spectral wavelengths that produces one hue to the stimulus energy of a narrow band of wavelengths that produces the same amount of opponent hue.

d. Achromatic responses in the Hurvich-Jameson theory are represented in terms of an experimentally determined foveal luminosity function [3.1.2c.2.].

10.5.3 By means of the equations developed for the Hurvich-Jameson theory, it has been possible to predict many of the generally known facts of normal and defective color vision with an encouraging degree of accuracy.

a. The Hurvich-Jameson theory has been shown to account systematically for the color perceptions associated with the basic stimulus variables, the facts of color mixture, color discrimination data, phenomena of chromatic adaptation, the Bezold-Brücke phenomenon, and reciprocal area-intensity effects [3, 4].

[10.5]

10.5.4   An attempt has been made with the Hurvich-Jameson theory to develop the mathematical framework for an ideal color system in which colors would be uniformly spaced according to differences in appearance, taking adaptation into account [6.5].

10.5.5   The Hurvich-Jameson theory, like the earlier Hering theory, assumes a physiological model that has been shown to be compatible with established physiological facts.

> **a.** The Hurvich-Jameson theory assumes that there is continuous spontaneous discharge in nerve fibers even when there is no direct stimulation, that the effects of stimulation are superimposed on the background of spontaneous activity, that there is opposed neural activity in the same fibers, that individual nerve fibers can never act independently, and that visual function involves integrated action of all units in the visual system; all these assumptions are verified by established physiological facts [2.2.4d.].

10.5.6   The Hurvich-Jameson theory had its origin in Hering's conception of a color mechanism but draws also on refinements made by Müller, Adams, Judd, and Granit.

> **a.** Although other theories developed from the basic Hering conception of a color mechanism also helped provide a basis for the Hurvich-Jameson theory, none had the substantial empirical basis provided by the chromatic response functions of Hurvich and Jameson.

10.5.7   The Hurvich-Jameson theory has the defects pointed out for the Hering theory [10.3.6].

Chapter Eleven

The Assessment of Color Aptitude

The ability to work with color may be assessed by comparative scores on tests in which color judgments of various types are made. All such tests should be administered only by personnel technically trained to do so (24, 200, 291).

11.1 The ability to work with color is called *color aptitude.*

11.1.1 Color aptitude is one of a variety of *special aptitudes* or abilities (as contrasted with a general ability) that a person may have.

a. Intelligence is considered to be a *general ability,* a common factor in a wide variety of special abilities. As a general ability that can be expected to enter into the development of many special abilities, intelligence might well be one of the factors in color aptitude (193).

b. Other special aptitudes that a person may have, besides color aptitude, are musical aptitude, mechanical aptitude, clerical aptitude, etc.

c. Color aptitude, as a species of special aptitude, may include a variety of even more specific aptitudes for particular tasks such as painting (art), color matching, and decorating.

11.1.2 Although color aptitude may be considered as a unitary special ability, it involves an interacting variety of factors which may be divided into two classes.

[11.1.2]

a. Color aptitude involves *native* or *inborn factors* such as intelligence, color vision, and several types of color-discrimination factors.

b. Color aptitude involves *acquired factors* caused by learning, such as the specific perceptual skills developed through training in making various kinds of color judgments. Color aptitude may be expected to improve with training.

11.2 Color aptitude may be assessed most reliably by an appropriate battery of tests, which sample different kinds of color judgments in which different native and acquired factors are operating.

11.2.1 A single test may sample only one kind of color judgment, like saturation discrimination or hue memory.

11.2.2 A variety of tests will sample a variety of skills that must be demonstrated in particular color occupations.

11.2.3 The number of tests used in assessing individuals for a color occupation will vary, depending on the skills required in that occupation.

11.2.4 Any test used in assessing individuals for color occupations should have high *reliability*, i.e., the result obtained from an individual should be repeatable within reasonable limits, so that a single test score can be expected to represent the individual's performance dependably. Correlation of scores on a test with those on a retest is called *test-retest reliability.*

11.2.5 Aptitude for a particular occupation can be assessed by relating weighted combinations of scores on different tests to success in that occupation. This procedure is called *validation* of a test battery and usually involves elaborate and expensive testing research and statistical treatment.

a. Validation of a test involves giving the test to a wide variety of people who are actually performing a given job.

b. Validation of a test involves correlating a set of test scores with some scaled criterion of job success.

c. If successful workers on a job consistently get high scores on a test and poor workers low scores, or vice versa, the test is said to have a high correlation with job performance, to be a good predictor for that job, and to have high *validity* for that job.

d. Most single tests will not have high validity but, if a battery

[11.2.5d.]

of several tests is used, some weighted combination of the test scores may prove to give somewhat higher validity.

1. Tests selected for use in a battery should be correlated with each other to find out which pairs of tests show low or zero intercorrelation.

a) Low or zero intercorrelation of tests shows they are measuring different factors.

b) If the kind of color judgment is different in different tests that have low intercorrelations, but each kind of judgment is involved in the color occupation under consideration, all such tests should be used in a test battery for that occupation.

c) In selecting tests for a battery, the color occupation should be analyzed to see what kinds of color judgments are required.

1) Tests should be developed (or found) to sample directly the color behavior found in the job of interest.

2) If tests are not available that sample directly the color behavior found in the job of interest, indirect tests may be used, but only after it has been found that results on such tests either have a high correlation with job success, or have a low correlation with other tests in a battery and the battery as a whole has high validity.

11.3 Certain tests are designed to measure *native or inborn color capacities* which show little if any improvement due to training. There are three general types of tests designed to measure native color capacities.

11.3.1 One general type of native color test measures color perception or *color vision* as such. Tests of this type are typically concerned with discriminatory responses to photopic stimulation of the small central region of the retina upon which we depend most in everyday life. There are three categories of color-vision tests [4.1].

a. The simplest type of color-vision test is *dichotomous*, designed to separate people with defective (red-green) color vision from those with normal color vision.

[11.3.1a.]

1. Dichotomous color-vision tests are used for general screening purposes where it is desired only to know who has a (red-green) color-vision defect regardless of the kind and amount of defect.

2. There are a variety of materials and kinds of judgment used in dichotomous color-vision tests. The tests used in assessing individuals for a particular occupation should be selected to include the material and kinds of judgment which are as directly applicable to the occupation as possible. Test scores should, however, always be correlated with some scaled criterion of job success.

a) The *Holmgren Wool Test* (HWT) is a dichotomous test which involves the sorting of chromatic wool samples into hue groups (132).

1) Materials for the HWT consist of 125 different chromatic skeins of wool and three larger standard or test skeins having Munsell designations of about 5 GY 7/6, 10 P 6/8, and 2 R 4/16.

2) On the HWT, the examinee must judge hue similarity by sorting the small skeins into three groups which produce hues most like those produced by the three standards.

3) The procedure on the HWT is for the examiner to throw down a test skein and ask the examinee to sort out eight or ten of the smaller skeins that seem to produce the same hue (loosely termed "color"). The procedure is repeated with the other two test skeins in turn.

4) The HWT has several defects which do not necessarily prevent use of the test in a particular selection situation where the materials and type of judgment may be appropriate.

(a) The HWT suffers from lack of standardization; there are many variations in object color from the original among the skeins.

(b) The HWT detects only about half of the color defectives examined, fails a number of "overanxious" normals, and permits easy practice improvement.

[11.3.1a.2.]

b) The *American Optical Company Pseudoisochromatic Plates* (AO plate test) comprise a dichotomous test which involves the perception of chromatic dot patterns on backgrounds of different chromatic dots (110).

1) Most of the plates in the AO plate test are a contemporary version of the most widely used of all color-vision tests, the so-called pseudoisochromatic (PIC) type that was originated by J. Stilling in Germany in 1876; other plates in the AO plate test are of the double-number type (color defectives read one number, normals another) and the camouflage type (color defectives read a number, normals see no number) developed by Ishihara.

2) A PIC plate or chart is a chromatic figure on a different chromatic background.

(a) Both the figure and background on a PIC plate are composed of many small dots or disks which vary irregularly in the lightness they produce and sometimes in size.

(b) The dots of the figure in a PIC plate produce chromaticness which is different from that produced by the dots in the background for normal color vision but do not produce such a difference for the type (or types) of defective color vision the PIC plate is intended to detect.

(c) The figure on a PIC plate is either an Arabic numeral or some other identifiable pattern.

3) A revised set of AO plates consists of 18 plates (selected from an original 46) which have the greatest diagnostic power.

4) The AO plates should be exhibited under standard viewing conditions, including a standard quality of illumination, with instructions to the examinee to report the figure or figures he perceives. Comparative data secured under tungsten light and daylight have shown that quality of illumination is an important test condition.

5) If the examinee fails on more than four of the AO plates, he is classified as (red-green) color defective.

[11.3.1a.2.b)]

6) The dichromat or anomalous trichromat has difficulty in perceiving particular patterns on the AO plates because they are distinguished from the background only by a red-green difference that he cannot discriminate [4.1.2, 4.1.3].
7) The number of AO plates failed is not a reliable indication of degree of defect, but the test has proved so valuable as a dichotomous device for separating normals from color defectives that much research has been stimulated.

c) There are PIC tests other than the AO plate test which have been developed since Stilling's time.

1) The Freeman Illuminant-Stable Color Vision Test (IST) is a PIC test which may be used with a variety of illuminants (80).

(a) The IST gives comparable results with illuminants having color temperatures ranging from 2000° to 14,000°K.
(b) The IST compares favorably in its dichotomous discrimination with the AO test.
(c) The IST employs configural patterns (digits) which are unfamiliar to many people who take the test, making it more difficult to administer and less reliable than other tests when used by untrained personnel.

2) Some of the plates of the Ishihara test are PIC plates (192).
3) Some of the Rabkin plates constitute a PIC test (111).
4) The Boström plates constitute a PIC test (26).
5) The Dvorine plates constitute a PIC test (65).

d) The *New London Navy Lantern Test* (NLT) developed by Farnsworth is the most recent development in a lantern-type color-naming dichotomous test (74).

1) The NLT was designed to screen out only the more severe forms of (red-green) color defect that are unsuited for naval and maritime occupations.
2) The NLT lantern presents paired chromatic lights si-

[11.3.1a.2.d)]

multaneously, and the examinee is asked merely to name the colors he perceives.

3) The NLT test-lights subtend very small visual angles, simulating distant signal lights.

4) The contrast of the paired test-lights in the NLT is varied to eliminate clues from everyday brightness-hue relations which, of course, could not be depended upon occupationally.

5) Red, green, and neutral filters are used in the NLT because they produce confusion colors for both common forms of dichromatic defect.

6) Test-retest reliability of the NLT is 0.95 (tetrachoric), based on 168 observers.

e) The *Farnsworth Dichotomous Test for Color Blindness* (Panel D-15) (FDT) is a test in which color chips are *arranged* in an order that, for normal color vision, is according to the hue produced but, for dichromatic vision, is according to the saturation produced (73).

1) The FDT was designed to separate severely (red-green) color-defective individuals from those normal and mildly (red-green) color-defective individuals who can make the color discriminations necessary in most routine industrial and military occupations.

2) The FDT materials consist of a rack containing fifteen Munsell papers (mounted in protective caps) which have the same (Munsell) value and chroma specification but differ in hue specification.

3) The FDT was standardized for administration under artificial daylight (about 6500°K).

4) The FDT is scored as either "passing" or "failing," but in this test many people with moderate color defect are passed (4 to 6 percent are failed compared to 8 to 9 percent on PIC tests).

b. The simplest type of color-vision test was called dichotomous; a second type of color-vision test is called *qualitatively diagnostic* because it is designed to classify the type but not the degree of defective color vision.

[11.3.1b.]

1. Very few tests of color vision are simply qualitatively diagnostic. They tend to be either dichotomous or to classify degree as well as type of defect. (Some tests, however, classify degree of defect without differentiating type.)

2. The Ishihara and Dvorine PIC tests are qualitatively diagnostic in the sense that, aside from their normal use as dichotomous tests, two of the plates in each test can be used to separate protanopes and deuteranopes.

3. The Farnsworth Dichotomous Test is qualitatively diagnostic in the sense that, aside from its normal use as a dichotomous test, the scored response pattern can differentiate protanopes, deuteranopes, and tritanopes.

c. The first and second types of color-vision tests were called respectively dichotomous and qualitatively diagnostic; a third type of color-vision test is called *quantitatively diagnostic* and may be designed to give either amount of red-green defect, without regard for kind, or both kind and amount of defect.

1. The *Sloan Color-Threshold Test* (CTT) is a quantitatively diagnostic test that makes use of the recognition of chromatic lights to measure degrees of red-green deficiency without distinguishing type of defect (248).

a) The CTT testing device provides for the presentation of eight different lights at each of eight different levels of luminous intensity. The intensity of the test lights at any given level is permanently adjusted to yield approximately equal difficulty in hue recognition for the normal observer.

b) On the CTT, the examinee is asked to name the color he perceives at each intensity level of each of the test lights.

c) On the CTT, part score for each of the eight test lights is the number of correct responses, counting from the highest intensity downward, before the first incorrect response is encountered; the maximum possible score on any part is the same as the number of luminance levels, or eight.

d) The CTT is essentially a threshold-color-naming test; the higher the intensity required for correct responses, the higher the threshold.

e) The errors on the CTT that are most characteristic of color-deficient observers include confusion of amber with

[11.3.1c.1.]

red and of green with white, inability to see red at low intensities, and failure on a particular light at higher but not at lower intensities. (Note that the scoring takes account of this last peculiarity, which suggests guessing.)

f) The CTT has been used for air-crew personnel because the lights were similar to those commonly encountered in practice, and scores on the test showed close agreement with performance on practical field tests.

g) Test-retest reliability on the CTT is 0.94, based on 55 observers.

2. The American Optical Company *Hardy-Rand-Rittler PIC Plate Test* (HRRT) is a quantitatively diagnostic PIC test that has been standardized to distinguish type and degree of red-green and yellow-blue defect (112).

a) The HRRT contains 21 PIC plates of four general types.

1) The HRRT has three demonstration plates showing respectively two, one, and no designs on a plate.
2) The HRRT has five screening plates for separating normal and defective color vision dichotomously.
3) The HRRT has nine qualitative and quantitative plates for diagnosing kind and amount of red-green defect.
4) The HRRT has four qualitative and quantitative plates for diagnosing kind and amount of yellow-blue defect.

b) In the HRRT only confusions of chromatic object-colors with neutral gray are used.

c) Since the HRRT uses simple designs, not letters, the test can be used with children, illiterates, and foreigners.

d) The HRRT is completely equivalent to the AO-plate test as a dichotomous screening device for red-green defects.

e) As a device to classify defective red-green vision into deutan and protan types, the HRRT is about as successful as the Nagel anomaloscope [11.3.1c.3.]; the HRRT was successful 97% of the time and the Nagel anomaloscope 98%, with no conflicts in classification.

f) A rating as to extent of defect by the HRRT showed 22.7% of defective observers to have a mild red-green defect, 30.7% a medium defect, and 46.7% a strong defect.

[11.3.1c.2.]

g) The HRRT is reported to have high reliability as a screening device, moderate reliability as a device for qualitative diagnosis, and rather poor reliability as a device for quantitative diagnosis.

h) The HRRT requires less than three minutes to administer.

3. A third kind of quantitatively diagnostic test of color vision is made with an instrument called an anomaloscope (AN). The most efficient of these tests is called the *Nagel anomaloscope* (288).

a) AN's are devices for mixing red and green lights in varying amounts to produce a metameric match for a yellow light.

1) An AN could be designed to mix any two lights to produce a metameric match for a third; the almost exclusive use of red and green to match yellow is due to the predominance of defects in red-green vision.

2) Over 99% of females and 90 to 92% of males match yellow with a red-to-green ratio that is within the limits of normal human variability.

3) Less than 1% of females and 8 to 10% of males match yellow with considerably more red or green than do normal observers, or with any mixture of red and green, provided the brightness of the yellow can be varied to match the mixture.

4) Individuals may be classified according to type and degree of red-green color defect depending on the ratio, and variation in the ratio, of red to green light required to match yellow using an AN.

5) Many forms of the AN have been developed since the 1890's, using various optical principles to accomplish the mixture of red and green.

b) Three types of color vision, normal, deutan, and protan, can be distinguished by the use of AN's. Within the deutan and protan types, most individuals can be classified further as moderately or severely deficient, but no clear dichotomy can be established between the moderate and severe groups [4.1.2, 4.1.3].

[11.3.1c.3.]

c) With an AN there is some overlap in the settings by anomalous cases with extremes of the normal distribution, and therefore AN's may not distinguish cases on the borderline of normal and anomalous vision when the examinees are untrained or have low color discrimination.

d) The most nearly adequate method of scoring AN results combines the amount of deviation from normal with the range of match variation in repeated settings.

> **1)** Neither deviation of AN match from normal nor matching range alone will adequately describe AN performance.
> **2)** A formula has been developed that reduces range and deviation of AN settings to one figure and that can be applied to all AN's so as to give comparable scores. This is called the *Willis-Farnsworth combination score* (288).

e) Since range of match is an important AN measure, adequate results with an AN cannot be expected unless the limits of an examinee's range of match are specifically explored while testing.

f) In a comparative study (288) it was found that of the instruments tested, the Nagel and then the Hecht-Schlaer instruments were the most efficient among several instruments for separating normals from anomalous examinees; the Nagel was entirely efficient, while the Hecht-Schlaer was nearly as good.

g) Diagnostic efficiency of an AN is related to the degree of metamerism between the yellow light and the mixture of the red and green component lights; the greater the degree of metamerism, the more diagnostic the instrument.

4. Pickford developed a quantitatively diagnostic test of color vision called the *Four-Color Test* (FCT) (214).

> **a)** The FCT is a variation of AN-type tests and tests yellow-blue as well as red-green vision.
> **b)** The FCT is an individual test, requiring only a few minutes testing time, which may be very useful in particular testing situations.

11.3.2 The first general type of test of native color ability included tests of color vision as such; a second general type of test

[11.3.2]

of native color ability is a visual *color-field* or *color-zone test*, which determines what parts of the retina give rise to particular colors.

a. Whereas tests of color vision as such are concerned only with a small central region of the retina, color-field or color-zone tests are used clinically to detect deviations from normality of both photopic and scotopic responses of the peripheral as well as the central retina [3.5.2, 3.7.2].

b. The general method in color-field tests is to use small standardized chromatic areas, which are moved into and out of the center of the visual field. The examinee is asked to report at what part of the field he "just sees" or "just does not see" color.

c. Color-field tests explore the visual field systematically so that a map can be drawn to show within what areas particular colors may be seen.

d. There are two kinds of visual color-field tests.

1. One kind of visual color-field test is called a perimetric test, or *perimetry*.

a) An instrument called a perimeter is used in perimetry. It consists typically of a quadrant rotating about one of its limiting radii as an axis so that at every point on this arm and at every angle (corresponding to some point on the retina) a color stimulus can be given and the visual impression recorded on a chart, the eye being placed at the center of the quadrant and fixated upon its center of rotation. Sometimes a semicircular arm is used, rotating about its middle radius.

2. A second kind of visual color-field test is called a campimetric test, or *campimetry*.

a) An instrument called a *campimeter* is used in campimetry.

b) A campimeter is an instrument with a flat chart for mapping the color sensibility of the whole retina.

c) In the campimeter, equal visual angles are represented by greater lengths as the distance from the fixation point increases, in accordance with the tangent function; it may be contrasted with the perimeter in which the instrumental determinations are proportional to the visual angles.

11.3.3 Two general types of tests of native color ability were called tests of color vision and color-field tests. *Tests of color discrimination* represent a third type of test of native color ability, although this type of test tends to overlap with tests of acquired color ability.

   a. There is probably no test that is completely unaffected by ability acquired through training.
   b. Some color-discrimination test results tend to be more affected by training than others.
   c. Color-discrimination tests classified here as *native* tend to give results that are *least* affected by training.
   d. Color-discrimination tests may be divided into two subclasses: *perceptual* and *memory*.

     1. *Perceptual color-discrimination tests* may be represented by the *Farnsworth-Munsell 100 Hue Test* (FMT) (73).

        a) The FMT may be used for several purposes.

           1) The FMT identifies varying degrees of perceptual *chromaticness* discrimination among persons with either normal or defective color vision.
           2) The FMT was not specifically designed as a dichotomous color-vision test but may be used with other tests to corroborate evidence for color deficiency; it discriminates tritans as well as protans and deutans.

        b) The FMT materials include four wooden panels and a total of 85 plastic caps in which chromatic samples are mounted.

           1) The test chips for the FMT produce for normal color vision a series of hues in Munsell notation equally spaced around the hue circle and of about equal Munsell value and chroma.
           2) Each wooden panel in the FMT contains about one-quarter of the 85 plastic caps arranged in random order.

        c) The FMT is administered under standard conditions of daylight illumination (preferably Macbeth Daylight).
        d) The examinee is instructed in the FMT to arrange the randomized test chips in consecutive order according to the

[11.3.3d.1.]

color responses produced and is allowed two minutes to do so for each of the four panels.

e) The FMT is scored in terms of errors made in arranging the test chips in proper order according to perceived chromaticness. Transpositions of test chips are indications of defective chromaticness discrimination.

f) The FMT makes it possible to sort people with normal color vision into three groups with respect to chromaticness discrimination: "superior," "normal," and "low."

2. *Memory* color-discrimination tests may be represented by the *Burnham-Clark-Munsell Color Memory Test* (BCMT) (39).

a) The BCMT identifies varying degrees of *successive* or *memory hue discrimination* among persons with normal color vision.

b) The BCMT was designed to be one of a possible battery of tests of color aptitude, but it can be used alone in specifically validated instances where hue memory is an important occupational factor.

c) The BCMT materials include a wheel on which test chips and comparison chips are mounted in concentric circles. The comparison chips consist of the 43 odd-numbered chips of the FMT [11.3.3d.1.]. Duplicates of 20 of these chips are used as test chips.

d) The BCMT is administered under standard conditions of daylight illumination (preferably Macbeth Daylight).

e) In the BCMT, a test chip is exposed to the examinee for 5 seconds, covered for 5 seconds, and then the examinee selects the comparison chip that looks most like the test chip previously exposed.

f) The BCMT is an individual-type test that takes 15 to 20 minutes to administer.

g) The BCMT is scored in terms of errors made in selecting the proper chip.

h) The BCMT makes it possible to sort people with normal color vision into three groups with respect to memory hue discrimination: "superior," "normal," and "low."

[11.3.3d.2.]

    i) Test-retest reliability of the BCMT is $0.64(\sigma_r = 0.07)$, based on a group of 80 observers.

    j) Validity of the BCMT has not been reported for specific occupations but must be empirically established for any particular occupation, usually in combination with other tests.

    k) The BCMT correlates with other tests as follows: ISCC-CAT 0.34 [11.4.5a.], WCAT 0.42 [11.4.5b.].

11.4 Certain tests are designed to measure native color capacities. Certain other tests are designed to measure *acquired color skills* developed through training in making various kinds of color judgments.

    11.4.1 Tests of acquired color skills also draw on inborn factors, but scores are influenced to a large degree by the amount of specific training a person has had.

    11.4.2 Confusion has arisen in the past because tests of acquired color skills frequently are called "color-aptitude" tests; color aptitude, as the ability to work with color, may imply a broader capacity than is typically assessed with a single test.

    11.4.3 Tests of acquired color skills are frequently called "color-aptitude" tests because the test designers have assumed, but rarely demonstrated, that test scores are highly correlated with performance in a wide variety of color occupations.

    11.4.4 Color aptitude is most likely to be assessed validly only by the procedure briefly described in 11.2.5.

    11.4.5 Two tests of acquired color skills have been developed which may be best used in combination with each other and with other tests in assessing color aptitude.

        a. The *Inter-Society Color Council Color Aptitude Test* (ISCC-CAT) requires a person to discriminate small differences in saturation and depends on experience as well as the inborn capacity to make such discriminations (59).

            1. The ISCC-CAT was developed as an aid in the selection of workers for color-matching and color-sorting occupations.

            2. The materials for the ISCC-CAT consist of two identical sets of 48 chromatic chips. One set is mounted according to hue on a test panel; the other set consists of loose chips in a fixed random order in a chip dispenser. Among chips produc-

[11.4.5a.]

ing the same hue, there are associated small saturation differences (in each of four hues) which are not easily discriminable.

3. The examinee is instructed on the ISCC-CAT to find a color match on the panel for each loose chip as he removes it from the chip dispenser.

4. The ISCC-CAT is scored in terms of the accuracy of the saturation matches; the greater the accuracy, the higher the score.

5. The ISCC-CAT is an individual-type test which requires about an hour to administer.

6. Perfect scores are unlikely on the ISCC-CAT and therefore, since scores distribute normally over the full range, the full range of ability to discriminate saturation differences can be measured.

7. The ISCC-CAT scores are not a measure of defective color vision; some color defectives become highly skilled in making fine color discriminations in certain hue regions and occasionally accumulate higher overall scores on this test than some people with normal color vision (279).

8. Test-retest reliability of the ISCC-CAT is 0.55, based on 200 observers.

9. Validity of the ISCC-CAT has not been reported for specific occupations but must be empirically established for any particular occupation, usually in combination with other tests.

10. The ISCC-CAT makes it possible to sort people, whether they have normal color vision or not, into five groups with respect to saturation discrimination: low, satisfactory, good, excellent, and exceptional.

b. The *Woods' Color Aptitude Test* (WCAT) is a color-memory test which requires a person to recognize the hue, saturation, and brightness of colors produced by patterns that may differ in form from patterns viewed a short time before (290).

1. The WCAT was developed as an aid in the selection of personnel for color occupations.

2. The materials for the WCAT are contained in a looseleaf book which contains 3 practice patterns, 25 test patterns, and 28 sets of 4 response patterns.

[11.4.5b.]

3. The examinee is instructed on the WCAT to look at a test pattern which is then removed and replaced by a set of four response plates, from which he chooses one or *none* of the response patterns as producing the same colors (regardless of pattern differences) as those produced by the test pattern.

4. The WCAT is an individual-type test (although 3 may be tested at once) that requires about one-half hour to administer.

5. The WCAT is not a measure of defective color vision, but is intended to call into play past color experiences, whether by a person with normal or defective color vision.

6. Test-retest reliability on the WCAT is 0.48, based on an independent check with a non-homogeneous group of 50 observers. Woods himself reported a coefficient of 0.86, based on a homogeneous group of 64 art students. Reliability is, however, usually a function of the homogeneity of background and training of the persons tested (290, 39).

7. The WCAT and ISCC-CAT correlate 0.39, and the WCAT and BCMT correlate 0.42. These relatively low "validity" coefficients suggest that these tests are measuring (at least partially) different factors, and that all three tests might be used in a test battery for assessing a more general color aptitude.

8. Validity of the WCAT was reported by Woods as a biserial validity coefficient of 0.76 when scores of 133 "non-colorists" were compared with those of 54 "colorists." This coefficient is suggestive rather than definitive because the biserial basis for computation was not obvious in the author's report (290).

9. The WCAT was correlated with the American Council on Education Psychological Examination (intelligence test) and produced a coefficient of 0.09, indicating little or no relationship to intelligence. This result suggests the possible use of both tests in situations where intelligence and color memory are required.

11.5 There is a generally acceptable procedure that should be followed in using tests to assess people for their ability to perform particular color occupations.

11.5.1 The use of color tests for selecting personnel should be undertaken only by, or under the supervision of, a fully trained

[11.5]

psychologist with a background specifically in technical color and testing.

11.5.2 Haphazard, unsystematic attempts by unqualified individuals to recommend tests for selecting personnel is fraught with pitfalls; expert counsel should always be requested.

Chapter Twelve

Experimental Color Aesthetics

There is as yet no extensive scientific knowledge about how colors affect people, but some start has been made in the experimental determination of the basic facts of color aesthetics (200).

12.1   The aesthetic significance of color is generally recognized in everyday life, but many scientists are skeptical regarding the capacity of color stimuli, as such, to evoke genuine affective responses like excitement, depression, pleasure, or other emotions, moods, and feelings.

12.1.1   The reality of affective responses to visual stimuli is not questioned, because they are often of the most violent and unmistakable nature.

12.1.2   Color stimuli, themselves, and not their roles as elements of complex stimulus patterns, are usually what is referred to when the affective responses to color stimuli are questioned by scientists.

12.2   Until the early part of the nineteenth century, the traditional approach to aesthetics (whether of color, music, or something else) was philosophical and deductive.

12.2.1   Traditionally the approach to aesthetics involved philosophical treatises that started with general principles on which there was no general agreement.

12.2.2   The traditional approach to aesthetics involved attempts to deduce rules of art which were seldom widely accepted or capable of universal application.

[12.2]

12.3 Fechner, the founder of psychophysics, felt that an empirical science of aesthetics was needed, not to supplant but to supplement the more philosophical treatises (291).

12.3.1 Fechner felt that aesthetics should be approached by gathering facts and working inductively toward principles as in any empirical science.

12.3.2 Aesthetic knowledge, experimentally established, has been limited for a long time to relatively simple facts, but these are at least clear and, whenever confirmed by other experimenters, command relatively universal acceptance.

12.3.3 In investigating aesthetic problems by experimental techniques, basic studies have first been made of individual likes and dislikes, choices, and preferences, i.e., individual reactions to simple sensory stimuli.

a. Pooling individual results by statistical procedures has led in some instances to group standards.

b. When individual differences are ironed out by averaging, aesthetic norms with some claim to validity are obtained, at least for a given group.

12.4 The facts of color aesthetics, until now at least, comprise only simple consistencies derived from the results of systematically designed experiments; the full groundwork has not yet been provided for more complex studies which should eventually deal directly with the total aesthetic experience in the complicated settings found in everyday life.

12.4.1 Laboratory studies of color aesthetics have so far made use mostly of the procedure in which an observer reports the impression or effect produced on him by an object presented to him. He must answer such questions as: "Is this object pleasing or displeasing?" "Which of two colors that you see is the more attractive?" "Are the colors perceived in this picture highly acceptable, moderately acceptable, neither acceptable nor unacceptable, moderately unacceptable, highly unacceptable?"

12.4.2 In a prolonged experiment in color aesthetics, dealing only with isolated objects, the observer's attitude may become that of a critic who must evaluate the merits of the object presented. His responses may become cool and matter-of-fact, with very little

[12.4]

feeling; he may make a report more about the object than his own affective state or his total aesthetic experience.

12.4.3   The results of experiments in color aesthetics dealing with simple objects have usually reflected judgment rather than feeling. As more complex objects in everyday surroundings are investigated, more and more feeling may be required in the observer's response.

12.4.4   The methods typically used in experimental studies of color aesthetics are pair comparisons, order of merit, successive categories, and absolute judgment.

> **a.** The *method of pair comparisons* involves stating a preference for one of a pair of objects, when all members of the class of objects are judged in all possible pairs.
>
> > **1.** Variations of the pair-comparison method, called triadic comparisons and paired-difference comparisons, are used for multidimensional analyses.
>
> **b.** The *method of order of merit* (*rank order*) involves ranking all members of a class of objects from high to low in the order of the observer's preference.
>
> **c.** The *method of successive categories* involves the placing of stimuli into one of several categories, each of which implies a different level of absolute preference.
>
> **d.** The *method of absolute judgment* involves making a preference judgment along a scale from "high" to "low" for each member separately of a class of objects.
>
> **e.** *Scaled preferences* for all members of a class of objects can be derived by well-known numerical analysis techniques for each of the methods used in experimental aesthetics.

12.5   Aesthetic preference for colors produced by single relatively isolated objects has been studied extensively, mostly with reflecting samples of moderate size, which produce relatively high saturation, such as chromatic papers a few square inches in area that produce fairly typical red, orange, yellow, green, blue, and violet hue responses.

> **12.5.1**   A combination of the data from 21,060 observers in 26 investigations on preference for single colors yields several results (71).

[12.5.1]

a. A weighted-average order of preference (from most to least preferred) for the six common hues based on the combined results of 26 investigations, in which there were considerable variations in results, is as follows:

1. Blue
2. Red
3. Green
4. Violet
5. Orange
6. Yellow

b. Based on the combined results of 26 investigations, the correlation between the order of color preference for men and for women is 0.95.

c. Based on the combined results from 26 investigations, the correlation between the order of color preference for Negroes and for whites is 0.96.

12.5.2 A listing of individual results from 31 studies on preferences for single colors shows a variety of colors reported as most or least liked [Table 12.1].

12.5.3 Systematic studies of preferences for single colors, in which the entire color solid was thoroughly sampled, showed that there are relations between the affective value (preference, pleasure) of a color and its three basic attributes (hue, saturation, and brightness) (104).

a. For single colors, as hue, saturation, or brightness changes continuously in a fixed direction, affective value also changes; the relationships are continuous but not simple.

b. For single colors, the relation of affective value to any one attribute of color is modified by changes in any other attribute, but in a systematic manner.

c. For single colors, when factors of size, illumination, background, type of observer, etc. are held constant, a prediction of average affective value can be accurately made from a knowledge of Munsell specifications of the sample.

d. For fully useful predictions of color preferences in practice, factors other than hue, saturation, and brightness must be subjected to systematic research, which has not been done.

Table 12.1   Preference for Single Colors

Authority	Description of Observers	Color Most Liked	Color Most Disliked
1. Garth and Collado, *J. comp. Psychol.*, 1929, **9**, 397	1000 Filipino children	Red	Yellow
2. Gesche, *J. comp. Psychol.*, 1927, **7**, 297	1100 Mexican children	Red	Orange
3. Garth, *J. exp. Psychol.*, 1922, **5**, 392	550 full-blooded Indians	Red	Yellow
4. Garth, *J. exp. Psychol.*, 1924, **7**, 233	1000 American white children	Blue	Yellow
5. Hurlock, *J. comp. Psychol.*, 1927, **7**, 389	400 white and Negro children	Blue	—
6. Imada, *Jap. J. Psychol.*, 1926, **1**, 1	1200 Japanese schoolchildren	Blue	Orange
7. Jastrov, *Pop. Sci. Mo.*, 1897, **50**, 361	3000 European males	Blue	
8. Jastrov, *Pop. Sci. Mo.*, 1897, **50**, 361	2000 European females	Red	
9. Katz and Breed, *J. appl. Psychol.*, 1922, **6**, 255	2500 American schoolchildren	Blue	Yellow and Orange
10. Lobsein, *Z. f. Psychol. u. Phys. d. Sinnesorgane*, 1904, **34**, 29	200 German schoolgirls	Red	Yellow
11. Michaels, *Amer. J. Psychol.*, 1924, **35**, 79	300 American schoolboys	Blue	Yellow and Green
12. Das Gupta and Basu, *Indian J. Psychol.*, 1936, **11**, 201	Bengali students	Green	
13. Das Gupta and Basu, *Indian J. Psychol.*, 1935, **10**, 81	Korus of Manipur Province	Yellow	
14. Aars, *Z. fur. pad. Psychol.*, I, 1899, **4**, 173	200 German children	Blue	Yellow
15. Arlitt and Buckner, *Proc. 35 Ann. Mtg. Amer. Psychol. Assn.*, 1925, 190	3-year-old white and Negro children	Red and Blue	Yellow and Green
16. Fernberger, *Amer. J. Psychol.*, 1914, **25**, 2448	15 American graduates	Red	Yellow
17. Farnsworth and Chickizola, *Amer. J. Psychol.*, 1931, **43**, 631	125 American boys	Red	Purple
18. Dorcus, *Ped. Sem.*, 1926, **33**, 399	Children (8–10 years)	Blue	Yellow
19. Hirohashi, *Jap. J. Psychol.*, 1926, I, 406	Young Japanese children	Red and Yellow	
20. Hirohashi, *Jap. J. Psychol.*, 1926, I, 406	Japanese children (higher grade)	Blue	Green
21. Holden and Bosse, *Arch. Ophthal.*, 1900, **29**, 261	30 infants under 1 year old	Red and Yellow	
22. Holden and Bosse, *Arch. Ophthal.*, 1900, **29**, 261	300 children (1–13 years)	Blue	Yellow and Orange
23. Mercer, *J. comp. Psychol.*, 1925, **5**, 109	1000 American Negroes	Blue	Yellow
24. Mercer, *Thesis*, Univ. of Texas, 1923	Mixed-blood Indians	Red	Yellow
25. Schulte, *Z. angew. Psychol.*, 1924, **24**, 42	60 European adults	Violet	Orange
26. Schuyten, *Exp. Padagogik.*, 1906, III, 102	4000 Dutch schoolchildren	Blue	Orange
27. Walton, Guilford, and Guilford, *Amer. J. Psychol.*, 1933, **45**, 322	1300 American university students	Blue	Yellow
28. Washburn, *Amer. J. Psychol.*, 1911, **22**, 114	35 American students	Red	Yellow
29. Allersch, *Psychol. Forsch.*, 1925, 6, I, 215	European adults	Blue	Yellow
30. Chon and Chen, *J. soc. Psychol.*, 1935, **6**, 290	500 Chinese high school students	White	Violet
31. Garth and Porter, *Amer. J. Psychol.*, 1934, **46**, 3, 448	1032 young children	Red	Yellow

M. E. Clarkson, O. L. Davies, and T. Vickerstaff, "Colour Harmony," pp. 81–99 in *Colour*, Great Britain: Imperial Chemical Industries, Ltd., 1950.

[12.5]

12.5.4 Degree of color preference varies because of differences in affective sensitivity to colors, as well as because of differences in the colors themselves (131).

   a. Some people are affected by colors more than the average person.
   b. Most people pay so little attention to colors unattached to familiar objects that their affective responses are weak or indifferent.
   c. When a person's attention is forced upon an isolated object color, as in an experiment, he can usually make an affective judgment of it, but the intensity of his experience is not necessarily typical of everyday life.

     1. As a general rule, affective responses to single colors are of low degree; they are aesthetic judgments which are partly intellectual and involve a minimum of emotionality.
     2. Only rarely are substantial affective responses made to single colors, and then only for a powerful stimulus or a strong association.

12.5.5 A number of characteristics of responses to single colors in experimental situations are known.

   a. *Affective reaction time* to single colors in experimental situations is slow relative to that of the initiating sensory responses; affective reaction time refers to the amount of time required for an affective response to appear after the stimulus is presented (209, 285).
   b. Aesthetic responses to single colors in experimental situations are subject to fatigue or adaptation; significant losses in affective value occur within a few seconds or minutes (53).

     1. Sometimes the observer gets "used to" or "tired of" a single color in an experimental situation.
     2. Sometimes perception of a single color in an experimental situation is so changed by adaptation or after-images that a different affective response is touched off.
     3. Pure affective adaptation to a single color in an experimental situation regularly tends to reduce either pleasantness or unpleasantness toward indifference.

[12.5.5]

    c. Change in intent or imagination may suffice to alter an affective judgment of isolated object colors (282).
    d. The area of an isolated object may influence the affective color response (284).

        1. Changes in area alter contrast effects and these changes influence affective value.
        2. Changes in area cause changes in perceived saturation and brightness, and these changes influence affective value.

12.5.6 Effects of object texture and mode of appearance on affective response to isolated object-colors have not been determined experimentally, but they are likely to be significant.

12.5.7 Facts have been experimentally established that show the origins of affective responses to single colors; significant trends of agreement among diverse groups certainly point to the operation of fundamental factors (4, 281).

    a. Children's color preferences develop and shift with age, showing a tendency to move from warm to cool colors with increasing years.
    b. Pleasurable and unpleasurable experiences sometimes influence color preferences (254).
    c. Preferences of special color workers sometimes shift toward pale, weak effects as experience increases.
    d. Standards of color preference develop on a basis of experience with a product.
    e. In general, most human responses are influenced by a mixture of native and acquired factors; it is impossible to avoid response modifications due to training and experience [11.1.2].

        1. *Acquired* responses due to training and experience are just as real as *native* (inborn) responses.
        2. Misunderstanding about the reality of acquired responses accounts for some of the skepticism of certain scientists regarding the reality of affective responses to color in general.

12.5.8 Preferences for combinations of simple chromatic patches, as well as for single chromatic patches, are marked by large variations among individuals in contradistinction to the rather small

[12.5]

variation of judgments made at different times by any particular person (63, 89).

12.5.9 When series of chromatic patches differing in affective value are viewed successively, the principle of affective contrast enhancement can operate.

a. The affective value of chromatic patches is raised when they are viewed after less pleasing chromatic patches or lowered when they are viewed after more pleasing chromatic patches. This is called the principle of *affective contrast enhancement* (18, 114).

b. Affective contrast enhancement is a general phenomenon which is not restricted to single colors, color combinations, or even vision.

c. In comparison with *perceptive* contrast enhancement [3.2.2a.], the results of *affective* contrast enhancement are sometimes remarkably persistent.

12.5.10 Results of studies on preferences for single colors are limited, and conclusions must be qualified.

a. Results of studies on preferences for single colors are expressed as averages and not as single reactions in single individuals at particular moments of time.

b. Predictions from studies on preferences for single colors may hold only for viewing and judging conditions comparable to those under which the results were obtained; they are based on assumptions that all other factors affecting preference were held constant.

c. It is possible, but needs to be demonstrated experimentally, that important everyday factors which may affect preferences for single colors do not entirely overshadow the sheer attributes of color as determiners of pleasure derived from color.

d. All conclusions regarding preference for single colors are based on the assumption that the affective value of a color depends directly on its hue, saturation, and brightness.

12.6 When two or more color stimuli in neighboring areas produce a pleasant affective response, they are said to produce a *color harmony*.

[12.6]

12.6.1   The facts of color harmony are few, since facts derive from the results of controlled experiments, and comparatively few investigations have been reported in this area.

a. The *law of affective combination* states that the affective value of a combination of colors is highly dependent on the affective values of the component colors (87, 103, 283).

1. The law of affective combination has been substantiated by studies of the intrinsic pleasantness of the simplest color combinations, for example, colors associated with two objects of equal area.
2. There are exceptions to the law of affective combination, some due to special art training and some due simply to the role played by form or configuration.
3. The law of affective combination holds for achromatic as well as for chromatic colors (183).
4. The law of affective combination does not require that the affective values of the components in a combination be *simply* additive.

b. In complex color combinations, even though they are abstract, the composition of the pattern carries greater weight than the associated colors in the determination of affective value.

1. In complex color combinations, the sophistication and attitude of the observer become increasingly important in the determination of the affective response.
2. An attempt to evaluate aesthetic patterns, based on Fechner's principle of "order in complexity," is shown in *Birkhoff's* (*22*) *aesthetic measure:*

$$M = O/C$$

where O stands for elements of order and C stands for elements of complexity in the composition in question.

a) The validity of Birkhoff's formula has been tested experimentally and disputed, pro and con (189).

1) One difficulty with Birkhoff's formula is ignorance of what weights to assign to the components.
2) A second difficulty with Birkhoff's formula is uncer-

[12.6.1b.2.a)]

tainty in identifying the elements to be taken into account in evaluating M.

3) Analysis of experimental data led Eysenck (72) to change Birkhoff's formula as follows:

$$M = OC$$

(a) Eysenck's formula takes account of Pope's fundamental criticism of the aesthetic measure, that it omitted quantity (225, 226).

(1) A single uniform chromatic expanse has maximum order and minimum complexity, yielding maximum aesthetic measure according to Birkhoff's formula, but there could obviously be *more;* a pattern that is too obvious lacks interest.

(2) In general, the more complexity that can be effectively ordered the better, for aesthetic value is enhanced by the more subtle patterns that greater complexity makes possible.

12.6.2 "Expert" opinion on color harmony, as contrasted with specific investigation, has been expressed in many books; contradictions in these opinions are frequent for several reasons.

a. Color harmony is a social concept since it is a matter of likes and dislikes, and affective responses vary from one person to another, and from time to time with the same person.

b. Color harmony depends on the absolute angular sizes of chromatic areas as well as on the design and the associated colors themselves.

c. Color harmony depends on the relative sizes of chromatic areas as well as on the associated colors themselves.

d. Color harmony depends on the shapes of the elements of the design as well as on the associated colors themselves.

e. Color harmony depends on the meaning or interpretation of the design as well as on the associated colors themselves.

f. Attempts to give simple rules for the construction of color harmonies are bound to fail to some extent; color harmony is a very complex subject, and preferences for color combinations

[12.6]

vary considerably depending on a multitude of social and cultural factors.

12.6.3 There are some generally accepted principles of color harmony that have stood the test of time. These half-truths are *not* scientifically verified but are simply the best guides to the selection of pleasing combinations of color stimuli that have been distilled from imperfect records of the thousands of trials and errors and partial studies so far made (160).

a. Color harmony results from colors selected according to an orderly plan which can be recognized and affectively responded to. This is called the *principle of order.*
b. Of two similar combinations of colors, that one will be most harmonious which is most familiar to the observer. This is called the *principle of familiarity.*
c. Any group of colors will be harmonious if, and to the degree that, the colors have a common aspect or attribute. This is the *principle of similarity.*
d. Color harmony can only be achieved by a combination of colors whose plan of selection is unambiguously evident. This is the *principle of unambiguity* and may be considered as a corollary of the principle of order.
e. Analysis of color harmony is usually based on representing colors by uniformly spaced points in a homogeneous, isotropic color space, so that relationships may be accurately described and more easily understood.

1. The *Munsell Book of Color* may be used to teach uniform color spacing because it shows uniformly spaced scales for hue, value, and chroma in daylight illumination [8.3.3c.].
2. The *Color Harmony Manual* (Container Corporation) does not serve well as an introduction to uniform color spacing, but it has important advantages in engineering color harmonies [8.3.2f.].

12.6.4 Other recommendations about color harmony refer in a general way to the structure of the design.

a. When there is a figure or localized region of principal interest in a design, it shows significant contrast with its less interesting surroundings.

[12.6.4]

b. There is some experimental evidence to show that the forms in which colors combine most pleasingly vary with the colors (41).

c. With reference to balance in a figure, there is some evidence to show that small areas producing a response of high saturation will balance large areas producing a response of low saturation.

> **1.** There is conflicting experimental evidence regarding the role of brightness in aesthetic balance when saturation and area are also considered (29, 94, 188).

d. If optimum color relations have been worked out for a composition of one size, they will probably need readjustment for the same composition in quite different size; differences that are pleasing in small size tend to become too great to be pleasing in large size.

e. Specific recommendations and even more general rules for design may quite frequently fail to bring desired results in color harmony; designs may prove to be pleasing which the "rules" say would be displeasing, and vice versa.

> **1.** Even if a rule for color harmony is completely valid for one situation, it cannot usually apply for all levels of design complexity.
>
> **2.** An aesthetic pattern is a dynamic whole, the elements of which interact with each other to affect size, shape, color, location, and higher-order characteristics.
>
> **3.** Some designs are so perfectly and delicately balanced that changing a single small detail may ruin the whole.

12.6.5 There is substantial experimental evidence that sensitivity to color harmony develops by experience as a function of age up through adolescence (57, 281).

12.6.6 There are substantiated sex differences in the appeal of certain color combinations.

12.6.7 There are few facts concerning the basic process of comparative aesthetic judgment itself.

> **a.** Different single colors are quite difficult to compare with respect to some one attribute such as saturation, but they can readily be compared for pleasantness.

[12.6.7]

    b. It is easily possible to compare different color combinations for pleasantness.

    c. A judgment of the relative pleasantness of different types of composition becomes progressively more difficult as the difference in type increases.

12.7 Colors perceived as belonging to a surface or volume are commonly associated with meaningful objects or compositions and may, therefore, be regarded as appropriate or inappropriate for particular purposes or applications. This association is called the *appropriateness of colors.*

    12.7.1 Colors are appropriate to the extent that they contribute to the beauty or efficiency of a design.

    12.7.2 A few experimental studies show significant agreement in the associations found between colors and names of moods (like gay, playful, leisurely, tender, sad, solemn, vigorous, exciting) (210, 234).

    12.7.3 Certain colors or color combinations are appropriate because they promote the functional efficiency of the visual mechanism, but in so doing they may contribute significantly to the well-being and pleasure of the individual.

12.8 Color combinations may produce strong emotional responses; whenever colors are responsible for conflict of ideas, purposes, or standards, there is the possibility of arousing a feeling of irritation, worry, or anger.

    12.8.1 The standards of utilitarian appropriateness and pure color harmony may conflict and thus be a cause of emotion.

    12.8.2 Strong emotion may be induced in women by color combinations because of conflicts between the dictates of fashion and flattery.

    12.8.3 Tampering with established object colors may be easily expected to produce strong emotional responses.

    12.8.4 Effective educational methods may intensify many of the complex and varied affective aspects of color.

12.9 There are several aspects of color that are not primarily affective but do possess aesthetic interest and are similar in the sense that they are derived reactions to color.

[12.9]

12.9.1   Apparent warmth, coolness, weight, and size are derived reactions to color.

a. Experimental studies show good agreement with respect to the fact that hue, more than brightness and saturation, contributes to impressions of warmth or coolness, with reliability coefficients of 0.95 and 0.82 respectively for warmth and coolness (48).

b. Three hundred people judged fifty equispaced Munsell hue samples and revealed a sharp "warmest" maximum for orange samples, but "coolest" ranged through the blues and greens (199).

c. There is good general agreement on studies of the apparent weight of colors to the effect that dark colors appear "heavy" and light colors less "heavy" (34, 58).

d. The effect of color on apparent size was studied and reliability coefficients of 0.93 and 0.91, respectively, were obtained for methods of observation and observers. Order of apparent size correlated 0.86 with luminance, and demonstrates that lighter objects look larger than darker objects of the same dimensions (107).

e. Older views with respect to the effect of color on apparent distance have been more recently reinterpreted (218).

1. It is often true that red-appearing surfaces "advance" and blue-appearing surfaces "recede"; the most effective stimulus basis, however, may be luminance rather than hue.

2. The relationship between apparent distance and luminance applies especially to small color samples in the surface or illuminant mode of appearance (151, 264).

12.10   The problems of color harmony are in a very unsettled state in general, and the need for an extended experimental attack is recognized.

12.10.1   Restrained use of accepted principles of color harmony is recommended for the novice, and then only in choosing color harmonies for preliminary check or getting a point of departure.

12.10.2   If a trial harmony appears exceptionally good, a contribution to aesthetic knowledge can be made by a careful record of the circumstances for future reference.

References

1. Abney, W. de W. On the change in hue of spectrum colors by dilution with white light. *Proceedings of the Royal Society*, 1910, **A83**, 120–127.
2. Adams, E. Q. A theory of color vision. *Psychol. Rev.*, 1923, **30**, 56–76.
3. Adams, E. Q. X-Z planes in the 1931 I.C.I. System of Colorimetry. *J. opt. Soc. Amer.*, 1942, **32**, 168–173.
4. Allen, E. C., and J. P. Guilford. Factors determining the affective values of color combinations. *Amer. J. Psychol.*, 1936, **48**, 643–648.
5. Allen, F. On reflex visual sensations. *J. opt. Soc. Amer. and Rev. Scient. Instr.*, 1923, **7**, 583–626.
6. Aubert, H. *Physiologie der Netzhaut.* Breslau: E. Morgenstern, 1865, p. 365.
7. Bacon, M. M., E. A. Rood, and M. F. Washburn. A study of affective contrast. *Amer. J. Psychol.*, 1914, **25**, 290–293.
8. Baird, J. W. *The color sensitivity of the peripheral retina.* Washington: Carnegie Institution, 1905.
9. Banister, H. A study in eye dominance. *Brit. J. Psychol.*, 1935–36, **26**, 32–48.
10. Barbrow, L. E. International commission on illumination. *J. opt. Soc. Amer.*, 1951, **41**, 734–741.
11. Bartleson, C. J. Some observations on the reproduction of flesh colors. *Phot. Sci. Eng.*, 1959, **3**, 114–117.
12. Bartleson, C. J. Memory colors of familiar objects. *J. opt. Soc. Amer.*, 1960, **50**, 73–77.
13. Bartlett, N. R., and R. Gagné. On binocular summation at threshold. *J. exp. Psychol.*, 1939, **25**, 91–99.
14. Bartley, S. H. Subjective flicker rate with relation to critical flicker frequency. *J. exp. Psychol.*, 1938, **22**, 388–394.
15. Bartley, S. H. *Vision.* New York: Van Nostrand, 1941, pp. 44–50.
16. Bartley, S. H. The features of the optic-nerve discharge underlying recurrent vision. *J. exp. Psychol.*, 1942, **30**, 125–135.
17. Bartley, S. H. The psychophysiology of vision. Ch. 24 in S. S. Stevens (Ed.), *Handbook of Experimental Psychology.* New York: John Wiley & Sons, Inc., 1951.
18. Beebe-Center, J. G. The law of affective equilibrium. *Amer. J. Psychol.*, 1929, **41**, 54–69.

221

19. Berry, W. Color sequences in the after-image of white light. *Amer. J. Psychol.*, 1927, **38**, 584–596.

20. Berry, W., and H. Imus. Quantitative aspects of the flight of colors. *Amer. J. Psychol.*, 1935, **47**, 449–457.

21. Bezold, W. von. Über das Gesetz der Farbenmischung und die Physiologischen Grundfarben. *Annalen der Physik*, 1873, **150**, 71–93, 221–247.

22. Birkhoff, G. D. *Aesthetic measure.* Cambridge, Mass.: Harvard University Press, 1933.

23. Blackwell, H. R. Contrast thresholds of the human eye. *J. opt. Soc. Amer.*, 1946, **36**, 624–643.

24. Boring, E. G. *Sensation and perception in the history of experimental psychology.* New York: D. Appleton-Century Co., 1942.

25. Boring, E. G., Langfeld, H. S., and Weld, H. P. *Foundations of psychology.* New York: John Wiley & Sons, 1951.

26. Boström, C. G., and I. Kugelberg. Official color sense control in Sweden. *Arch. Ophthal.* (Chicago), 1947, **38**, 378–380.

27. Bouma, P. J. *Physical aspects of color.* New York: Elsevier Book Publ., 1949.

28. Boynton, R. M. Theory of color vision. *J. opt. Soc. Amer.*, 1960, **50**, 929–944.

29. Bradley, M. C., Jr. A theory of tone attraction. *Tech. Studies in the Field of Fine Arts*, 1933, **2**, 1–10.

30. Breneman, E. J. Dependence of luminance required for constant brightness upon chromaticity and chromatic adaptation. *J. opt. Soc. Amer.*, 1958, **48**, 228–232.

31. Bridgman, P. W. *The logic of modern physics.* New York: The MacMillan Co., 1927.

32. Broca, A., and D. Sulzer. La sensation lumineuse en fonction du temps. *Comptes Rendus, Académie des Sciences*, Paris, 1902, **134**, 831–834; 1903, **137**, 944–946, 977–979, 1046–1049.

33. Brunswik, E. *Wahrnehmung und Gegenstandswelt.* Leipzig: Deutisvie, 1934.

34. Bullough, E. On the apparent heaviness of colours. *Brit. J. Psychol.*, 1906–1908, **2**, 111–152.

35. Burnham, R. W. The dependence of color upon area. *Amer. J. Psychol.*, 1951, **64**, 521–533.

36. Burnham, R. W. Comparative effects of area and luminance on color. *Amer. J. Psychol.*, 1952, **65**, 27–38.

37. Burnham, R. W. Bezold's color-mixture effect. *Amer. J. Psychol.*, 1953, **66**, 377–385.

38. Burnham, R. W. Binocular subjective colors and the visual mechanism. *Amer. J. Psychol.*, 1954, **67**, 492–499.

39. Burnham, R. W., and J. R. Clark. A test of hue memory. *J. appl. Psychol.*, 1955, **39**, 164–172.

40. Burnham, R. W., R. M. Evans, and S. M. Newhall. Prediction of color appearance with different adaptation illuminations. *J. opt. Soc. Amer.*, 1957, **47**, 35–42.

41. Campbell, I. G. A study of the fitness of color combinations, in duple and in triple rhythm, to line designs. *J. exp. Psychol.*, 1942, **30**, 311–325.

42 Chapanis, A. Relationships between age, visual acuity, and color vision. *Human Biology*, 1950, **22**, 1–33.

43. Chapanis, A., and R. M. Halsey. Luminance of equally bright colors. *J. opt. Soc. Amer.*, 1955, **45**, 1–6.

44. Chase, W. P. Color vision in infants. *J. exp. Psychol.*, 1937, **20**, 203–222.

45. Clark, B., M. L. Johnson and R. E. Dreher. The effect of sunlight on dark adaptation. *Amer. J. Ophthal.*, 1946, **29**, 828–836.

46. Cohen, J. Color adaptation of the human eye. *Amer. J. Psychol.*, 1946, **59**, 84–110.

47. Cohen, J., and D. A. Gordon. The Prevost-Fechner-Benham subjective colors. *Psychol. Bull.*, 1949, **46**, 97–136.

48. Collins, N. *The appropriateness of certain color combinations in advertising.* Master of Arts Thesis, Columbia University, New York, 1924.

49. Committee on Colorimetry, Optical Society of America. *The Science of Color.* New York: Thomas Y. Crowell Co., 1953.

50. Condon, E. Y., and H. Odishaw (*Eds.*) *Handbook of physics.* New York: McGraw-Hill Book Co., Inc., 1958.

51. Craik, K. J. W. The effect of adaptation on differential brightness discrimination. *J. Physiol.*, 1938, **92**, 406–421.

52. Crawford, B. H. Ocular interaction in its relation to measurements of brightness threshold. *Proceedings of the Royal Society*, 1939–1940, **B128**, 552–559.

53. Crawford, D., and M. F. Washburn. Fluctuations in the affective value of colors during fixation for one minute. *Amer. J. Psychol.*, 1911, **22**, 579–582.

54. Crosland, H. R., and I. Anderson. The effects of eye-dominance on 'range of attention' scores. *University of Oregon Studies in Psychology*, 1933, **1**, 23.

55. Crosland, H. R., and C. E. Buxton. The concept 'eye-preference.' *Amer. J. Psychol.*, 1937, **49**, 458–461.

56. Dagher, M., A. Cruz, and L. Plaza. Colour thresholds with monochromatic stimuli in the spectral region 530 to 630 mμ. In *National Physical Laboratory Symposium No. 8: Visual Problems of Colour*, Vol. 2, 387–398. London: Her Majesty's Stationery Office, 1958.

57. Dashiell, J. F. Children's sense of harmonies in colors and tones. *J. exp. Psychol.*, 1917, **2**, 466–475.

58. DeCamp, J. E. The influence of color on apparent weight. A preliminary study. *J. exp. Psychol.*, 1917, **2**, 347–370.

59. Dimmick, F. L. Specifications and calibration of the 1953 edition of the Inter-Society Color Council Color Aptitude Test. *J. opt. Soc. Amer.*, 1956, **46**, 389–393.

60. Ditchburn, R. W. *Light.* New York: Interscience Publishers, 1953.

61. Ditchburn, R. W. Eye movements and visual perception. *Research*, 1956, **9**, 466–471.

62. Ditchburn, R. W., D. H. Fender, and S. Mayne. Vision with controlled movements of the retinal image. *J. Physiol.* (London), 1959, **145**, 98–107.

63. Dorcus, R. M. Color preferences and color associations. *J. genet. Psychol.*, 1926, **33**, 399–434.

64. Duke-Elder, W. S. *Textbook of ophthalmology*. St. Louis: C. V. Mosby Co., 1932, p. 436.

65. Dvorine, I. A new diagnostic method of testing and training color perception. *Amer. J. Optom.*, 1944, **21**, 225–235.

66. Evans, R. M. Visual processes and color photography. *J. opt. Soc. Amer.*, 1943, **33**, 579–614.

67. Evans, R. M. *An introduction to color*. New York: John Wiley & Sons, Inc., 1948.

68. Evans, R. M. Light sources and colored objects. *Illuminating Engineering*, 1949, **44**, 47–54.

69. Evans, R. M. On some aspects of white, gray, and black. *J. opt. Soc. Amer.*, 1949, **39**, 774–779.

70. Evans, R. M. Fluorescence and gray content of surface colors. *J. opt. Soc. Amer.*, 1959, **49**, 1049–1059.

71. Eysenck, H. J. A critical and experimental study of colour preferences. *Amer. J. Psychol.*, 1941, **54**, 385–394.

72. Eysenck, H. J. The experimental study of the 'good Gestalt'—A new approach. *Psychol. Rev.*, 1942, **49**, 344–364.

73. Farnsworth, D. The Farnsworth-Munsell 100-hue and dichotomous tests for color vision. *J. opt. Soc. Amer.*, 1943, **33**, 568–578.

74. Farnsworth, D., and P. Foreman. Development and trial of New London Navy lantern as a selection test for serviceable color vision. *Color Vision Report No. 12*, Medical Research Department, U.S. Submarine Base, New London, Conn., 1946.

75. Ferguson, H. H., and T. P. H. McKellar. The influence of chromatic light stimulation on the subsequent rate of perception under conditions of low illumination. *Brit. J. Psychol.*, 1943–44, **34**, 81–88.

76. Ferry, E. S. Persistence of vision. *American Journal of Science*, 1892, **44**, 192–207.

77. Fierz-David, H. E., and L. Blangey. (Trans. by P. W. Vittum). *Fundamental processes of dye chemistry*. New York: Interscience Publishers, 1949.

78. Fieser, L. F., and M. Fieser. *Organic chemistry*. New York: Reinhold Publishing Corp., 1956, Chap. 36.

79. Foss, C. E., D. Nickerson, and W. C. Granville. Analysis of the Ostwald Color System. *J. opt. Soc. Amer.*, 1944, **34**, 361–381.

80. Freeman, E. An illuminant-stable color vision test, I. *J. opt. Soc. Amer.*, 1948, **38**, 532.

81. Fry, G. A. New observations related to the problem of color-contrast. *J. exp. Psychol.*, 1934, **17**, 798–804.

82. Fry, G. A. Color sensations produced by intermittent white light and the three-component theory of color-vision. *Amer. J. Psychol.*, 1935, **47**, 464–469.

83. Fry, G. A. Mechanisms subserving simultaneous brightness contrast. *Amer. J. Optom. and Arch. Amer. Acad. Optom.*, 1948, Monograph 45, 17 pp.

84. Fuchs, W. The influence of form on the assimilation of colours. Sel. 7 in: *A source book of Gestalt psychology*, by W. D. Ellis. New York: Harcourt, Brace, & Co., 1938, 95–108.

85. Galifret, Y., and H. Piéron. Les spécificités de persistance des impressions chromatiques fondamentales. *Revue d'Optique,* 1949, **28,** 154–156.
86. Wallach, H., and A. Galloway. The constancy of colored objects in colored illumination. *J. exp. Psychol.,* 1946, **36,** 119–126.
87. Geissler, L. R. The affective tone of color combinations. In *Studies in psychology contributed by colleagues and former students of E. B. Fitchener.* Worcester: L. N. Wilson, 1917, 150–174.
88. Gelb, A. Die "Farbenkonstanz" der Sehdinge. *Handbuch der normalen und pathologischen Physiologie,* 12/1. Berlin: J. Springer, 1929, pp. 594–678.
89. Gordon, K. A study of esthetic judgments. *J. exp. Psychol.,* 1923, **6,** 36–43.
90. Graham, C. H. An investigation of binocular summation: I The fovea. *J. gen. Psychol.,* 1930, **3,** 494–510.
91. Graham, C. H. An investigation of binocular summation: II The periphery. *J. gen. Psychol.,* 1931, **5,** 311–328.
92. Graham, C. H. Color theory. In S. Koch, Ed.: *Psychology: A study of a science, Study I, Vol. I.* New York: McGraw-Hill Book Co., Inc., 1959, pp. 145–287.
93. Le Grand, Y. *Light, colour, and vision.* New York: John Wiley & Sons, Inc., 1957.
94. Granger, G. W. Area balance in color harmony: An experimental study. *Science,* 1953, **117,** 59–61.
95. Granit, R. *Sensory mechanisms of the retina.* London: Oxford Univ. Press, 1947.
96. Granit, R. *Receptors and sensory perception.* New Haven: Yale Univ. Press, 1955.
97. Granville, W. C., and E. Jacobson. Colorimetric specification of the *Color Harmony Manual* from spectro-photometric measurements. *J. opt. Soc. Amer.,* 1944, **34,** 382–395.
98. Granville, W. C., C. E. Foss, and I. H. Godlove. *Color Harmony Manual:* Colorimetric analysis of third edition. *J. opt. Soc. Amer.,* 1950, **40,** p. 265A. Abstract.
99. Grassmann, H. Zur Theorie der Farbenmischung. *Poggendorf's Ann.,* 1853, **89,** 69; also *Philosophical Magazine,* 1853, **7,** 254.
100. Gray, D. E. (*Ed.*) *American Institute of Physics Handbook.* New York: McGraw-Hill Book Co., Inc., 1957.
101. Grether, W. F. The magnitude of simultaneous color contrast and simultaneous brightness for chimpanzee and man. *J. exp. Psychol.,* 1942, **30,** 69–83.
102. Griffin, D. R., R. Hubbard, and G. Wald. The sensitivity of the human eye to infra-red radiation. *J. opt. Soc. Amer.,* 1947, **37,** 546–554.
103. Guilford, J. P. The prediction of affective values. *Amer. J. Psychol.,* 1931, **43,** 469–478.
104. Guilford, J. P. The affective value of color as a function of hue, tint, and chroma. *J. exp. Psychol.,* 1934, **17,** 342–370.
105. Guilford, J. P. *Psychometric methods* (2nd Ed.). New York: McGraw-Hill Book Co., Inc., 1954.

106. Gulliksen, H., and S. Messick (*Eds.*) *Psychological scaling.* New York: John Wiley & Sons, 1960, Chaps. 12, 13, & 14.

107. Gundlach, C., and C. Macoubrey. The effect of color on apparent size. *Amer. J. Psychol.*, 1931, **43**, 109–111.

108. Haig, C. The course of rod dark adaptation as influenced by the intensity and duration of pre-adaptation to light. *J. gen. Physiol.*, 1941, **24**, 735–751.

109. Hanes, R. M. Suprathreshold area brightness relationships. *J. opt. Soc. Amer.*, 1951, **41**, 28–31.

110. Hardy, L. H., G. Rand, and M. C. Rittler. A screening test for defective red-green vision. *J. opt. Soc. Amer.*, 1946, **36**, 610–614.

111. Hardy, L. H., G. Rand, and M. C. Rittler. The Rabkin test as a means of detecting and analyzing defective color vision. *J. gen. Psychol.*, 1947, **36**, 189–206.

112. Hardy, L. H., G. Rand, and M. C. Rittler. H-R-R polychromatic plates. *J. opt. Soc. Amer.*, 1954, **44**, 509–523.

113. Harrington, R. E. Effect of color temperature on apparent brightness. *J. opt. Soc. Amer.*, 1954, **44**, 113–116.

114. Harris, A. J. An experiment on affective contrast. *Amer. J. Psychol.*, 1929, **41**, 617–624.

115. Hartridge, H. The change from trichromatic to dichromatic vision in the human retina. *Nature*, 1945, **155**, 657–662.

116. Heath, G. G. Luminosity curves of normal and dichromatic observers. *Science*, 1958, **128**, 775–776.

117. Hecht, S. Intensity discrimination. *Cold Spring Harbor Symposia on Quantitative Biology*, 1935, **3**, 230–236.

118. Hecht, S., J. C. Peskin, and M. Patt. Intensity discrimination in the human eye. *J. gen. Physiol.*, 1939, **22**, 7–19.

119. Helmholtz, H. *Treatise on physiological optics: The perceptions of vision.* J. P. C. Southall, edit. Vols. II & III. New York: Optical Society of America, 1924–25.

120. Helms, A., and R. Prehn. Empfindlichkeitsänderungen des dunkeladaptierten menschlichen Auges bei monocularer Adaptation in Abhängigkeit vom Helladaptationsniveau. *v. Graefes Arch. Ophthal.*, 1958, **160**, 285–289.

121. Helms, A., and J. Raeuber. Über Empfindlichkeitsänderungen des monocular dunkeladaptierten Auges bei verschiedenfarbiger Helladaptation des anderen Auges. *v. Graefes Arch. Ophthal.*, 1958, **160**, 290–292.

122. Helson, H. The effects of direct stimulation of the blind spot. *Amer. J. Psychol.*, 1929, **41**, 345–397.

123. Helson, H. Fundamental problems in color vision. I. The principle governing changes in hue, saturation, and lightness of non-selective samples in chromatic illumination. *J. exp. Psychol.*, 1938, **23**, 439–476.

124. Helson, H. Adaptation level theory. In S. Koch (*Ed.*), *Psychology: A study of a science.* Vol. I. New York: McGraw-Hill Book Co., Inc., 1959.

125. Helson, H., and J. Grove. Changes in hue, lightness, and saturation of surface colors in passing from daylight to incandescent-lamp light. *J. opt. Soc. Amer.*, 1947, **37**, 387–395.

126. Helson, H., and V. B. Jeffers. Fundamental problems in color vision.

II. Hue, lightness, and saturation of selective samples in chromatic illumination. *J. exp. Psychol.*, 1940, **26**, 1–27.

127. Helson, H., and D. B. Judd. A study in photopic adaptation. *J. exp. Psychol.*, 1932, **15**, 380–398.

128. Helson, H., and F. H. Rohles, Jr. A quantitative study of reversal of classical lightness-contrast. *Amer. J. Psychol.*, 1959, **72**, 530–538.

129. Henneman, R. H. A photometric study of the perception of object color. *Arch. Psychol.*, 1935, No. 179. 88 pp.

130. Hering, E. Beitrag zur Lehre vom Simultankontrast. *Zeitschrift für Psychologie und Physiologie der Sinnesorgane*, 1890, **1**, 18–28.

131. Hevner, K. The aesthetic experience: A psychological description. *Psychol. Rev.*, 1937, **44**, 245–263.

132. Holmgren, F. On the theory and diagnosis of colour-blindness. *Report of the Smithsonian Institute*, 1877–1878 ed.

133. Hulburt, E. O. Time of dark adaptation after stimulation by various brightnesses and colors. *J. opt. Soc. Amer.*, 1951, **41**, 402–404.

134. Hunt, R. W. G. Visual adaptation and the apparent saturation of colors. *Proceedings of the Physical Society*, 1949, **62B**, 203–206.

135. Hunt, R. W. G. The effects of daylight and tungsten light-adaptation on color perception. *J. opt. Soc. Amer.*, 1950, **40**, 362–371.

136. Hunt, R. W. G. Light and dark adaptation and the perception of color. *J. opt. Soc. Amer.*, 1952, **42**, 190–199.

137. Hunt, R. W. G. The perception of color in 1° fields for different states of adaptation. *J. opt. Soc. Amer.*, 1953, **43**, 479–484.

138. Hurvich, L. M., and D. Jameson. A quantitative theoretical account of color vision. *Trans. N.Y. Acad. Sci.*, 1955, **18**, 33–38.

139. Hurvich, L. M., and D. Jameson. Some quantitative aspects of an opponent-colors theory. II. Brightness, saturation, and hue in normal and dichromatic vision. *J. opt. Soc. Amer.*, 1955, **45**, 602–616.

140. Hurvich, L. M., and D. Jameson. Some quantitative aspects of an opponent-colors theory. IV. A psychological color specification system. *J. opt. Soc. Amer.*, 1956, **46**, 416–421.

141. Hurvich, L. M., and D. Jameson. An opponent-process theory of color vision. *Psychol. Rev.*, 1957, **64**, 384–404.

142. International Commission on Illumination. Proceedings of the Sixth Session (Geneva), 1924.

143. International Printing Ink Corporation, Research Laboratories. Color chemistry. *Int. Print. Ink Corp.*, 1935.

144. ISCC-NBS. The ISCC-NBS method of designating colors and a dictionary of color names. National Bureau of Standards Circular #553, 1955. See Ref. No. 167.

145. Jameson, D., and L. M. Hurvich. The binocular fusion of yellow in relation to color theories. *Science*, 1951, **114**, 199–202.

146. Jameson, D., and L. M. Hurvich. Some quantitative aspects of an opponent-colors theory. I. Chromatic responses and spectral saturation. *J. opt. Soc. Amer.*, 1955, **45**, 546–552.

147. Jameson, D., and L. M. Hurvich. Some quantitative aspects of an opponent-colors theory. III. Changes in brightness, saturation, and hue with chromatic adaptation. *J. opt. Soc. Amer.*, 1956, **46**, 405–415.

148. Jameson, D., and L. M. Hurvich. Theoretical analysis of anomalous tri-chromatic color vision. *J. opt. Soc. Amer.,* 1956, **46,** 1075–1089.
149. Jameson, D., and L. M. Hurvich. Perceived color and its dependence on focal, surrounding, and preceding stimulus variables. *J. opt. Soc. Amer.,* 1959, **49,** 890–898.
150. Jenkins, F. A., and H. E. White. *Fundamentals of physical optics.* New York: McGraw-Hill, 1937.
151. Johns, E. H., and F. C. Summer. Relation of the brightness differences of colors to their apparent distances. *J. Psychol.,* 1948, **26,** 25–29.
152. Johnson, R. C. *An introduction to molecular spectra.* New York: Pitman, 1949.
153. Judd, D. B. A quantitative investigation of the Purkinje after-image. *Amer. J. Psychol.,* 1927, **38,** 507–533.
154. Judd, D. B. Least retinal illumination by spectral light required to evoke the "blue arcs of the retina." *J. Res. Nat. Bur. Stds.,* 1929, **2,** 441–451.
155. Judd, D. B. Chromaticity sensibility to stimulus differences. *J. opt. Soc. Amer.,* 1932, **22,** 72–108.
156. Judd, D. B. Estimation of chromaticity differences and nearest color temperature on the Standard 1931 ICI Colorimetric Coordinate System. *J. Res. Nat. Bur. Stds.,* 1936, **17,** 771–779.
157. Judd, D. B. Hue, saturation, and lightness of surface colors with chromatic illumination. *J. Res. Nat. Bur. Stds.,* 1940, **24,** 293–333.
158. Judd, D. B. Basic correlates of the visual stimulus. Ch. 22 in S. S. Stevens (*Ed.*), *Handbook of Experimental Psychology,* New York: John Wiley & Sons, Inc., 1951.
159. Judd, D. B. *Color in Business, Science, and Industry.* New York: John Wiley & Sons, Inc., 1952.
160. Judd, D. B. Classic laws of color harmony expressed in terms of the color solid. *ISCC Newsletter,* No. 119, **13,** 1955.
161. Karwoski, T. F., and M. N. Crook. Studies in the peripheral retina: I. The Purkinje after-image. *J. gen. Psychol.,* 1937, **16,** 323–356.
162. Karwoski, T. F., and W. B. Perry. Studies in the peripheral retina: III. The Purkinje after-image bulge. *J. gen. Psychol.,* 1943, **29,** 63–85.
163. Karwoski, T. F., and H. Warrener. Studies in the peripheral retina: II. The Purkinje after-image on the near foveal area of the retina. *J. gen. Psychol.,* 1942, **26,** 129–151.
164. Katona, G. Zur Analyse der Helligkeitskonstanz. *Psychologische Forschung,* 1929, **12,** 94–126.
165. Katz, D. *The world of colour.* London: Kegan Paul, Trench, Trubner, & Co., Ltd., 1935, p. 164.
166. Keller, M. Ocular dominance and the range of visual apprehension. *J. exp. Psychol.,* 1937, **21,** 545–553.
167. Kelley, K. L., and D. B. Judd. The ISCC-NBS method of designating colors and a dictionary of color names. National Bureau of Standards Circular #553, 1955.
168. Kherumian, R., and R. W. Pickford. *Hérédité et fréquense des anomalies congénitales du sens chromatique (dyschromatopsies).* Paris: Vigot Frères, 1959.

169. Kries, J. von. Beitrag zur Physiologie der Gesichtsempfindungen. *Archiv für Anatomie und Physiologie* (Physiologische Abteilung), 1878, **2**, 503–524.

170. Kries, J. von. Die Gesichtsempfindungen. In *Handbuch der Physiologie des Menschen.*, Vol. III. Braunschweig: Vieweg, 1905, 109–282.

171. Kubelka, P., and F. Munk. Ein Beitrag zur Optik der Farbanstriche. *Z. tech. Physik*, 1931, **12**, 593–601.

172. Land, E. H. Color vision and the natural image. Part I. *Proc. Nat. Acad. Sci.*, 1959, **45**, 115–129. Part II, 636–644.

173. Land, E. H. Experiments in color vision. *Scientific American*, 1959, **200**, 84–94, 96, 99.

174. Lowry, E. M. Some experiments with binocular and monocular vision. *J. opt. Soc. Amer.*, 1929, **18**, 29–40.

175. MacAdam, D. L. Loci of constant hue and brightness determined with various surrounding colors. *J. opt. Soc. Amer.*, 1950, **40**, 589–595.

176. MacAdam, D. L. Perceptions of colors in projected and televised pictures. *J. Soc. Motion Picture Tel. Eng.*, 1956, **65**, 455–469.

177. MacAdam, D. L. Beat-frequency hypothesis of colour perception. In *National Physical Laboratory Symposium No. 8: Visual problems of colour*, Vol. 2, 579–601. London: Her Majesty's Stationery Office, 1958.

178. MacLeod, R. B. Brightness-constancy in unrecognized shadows. *J. exp. Psychol.*, 1940, **27**, 1–22.

179. MacLeod, R. B. An experimental investigation of brightness constancy. *Arch. Psychol.*, 1932, No. 135. 102 pp.

180. Marshall, B. H., and J. P. Guilford. The dependence of hue, tint and chroma upon area. *Amer. J. Psychol.*, 1934, **46**, 465–469.

181. McDougall, W. The variation of the intensity of visual sensation with the duration of the stimulus. *Brit. J. Psychol.*, 1904–05, **1**, 151–189.

182. McGregor, D. Sensitivity of the eye to the saturation of colors. *J. exp. Psychol.*, 1936, **19**, 525–546.

183. Metcalf, J. T. The pleasantness of brightness combinations. *Amer. J. Psychol.*, 1927, **38**, 607–623.

184. Middleton, W. E. K., and M. C. Holmes. The apparent colors of surfaces of small subtense — a preliminary report. *J. opt. Soc. Amer.*, 1949, **39**, 582–592.

185. Miescher, K. and R. Rometsch. Zur experimentellen Teilung des Farbenraumes. *Die Farbe*, 1955, **4**, 281–284.

186. Miles, W. R. Ocular dominance in human adults. *J. gen. Psychol.*, 1930, **3**, 412–430.

187. Mitchell, A. C. G., and M. W. Zemansky. *Resonance radiation and excited atoms.* Cambridge (Eng.) University Press, 1934.

188. Moon, P., and D. E. Spencer. Aesthetic measure applied to color harmony. *J. opt. Soc. Amer.*, 1944, **34**, 234–242.

189. Moon, P., and D. E. Spencer. Area in color harmony. *J. opt. Soc. Amer.*, 1944, **34**, 93–103.

190. Müller, G. E. *Darstellung und Erklärung der verschiedenen typen der Farbenblindheit nebst Erörterung der Funktion des Stäbchenapparates sowie des Farbensinns der Biene und der Fische.* Göttingen: Vandenhoeck & Ruprecht, 1924.

191. Müller, G. E.   Über die Farbenempfindungen.   Bd. 2, *Zeits. Psychol. Physiol. Sinnesorg.*, 1930, Ergänzungsbd., **17**, 1–430; **18**, 435–647.
192. Murray, E.   The Ishihara Test for color-blindness: A point in ethics. *Amer. J. Psychol.*, 1935, **47**, 511–513.
193. Murray, E.   Evolution of color vision tests.   *J. opt. Soc. Amer.*, 1943, **33**, 316–334.
194. Murray, H. P.   *Colour in theory and practice.*   London: Chapman & Hall, 1952.
195. Newhall, S. M.   The control of eyelid movements in visual experiments. *Amer. J. Psychol.*, 1932, **44**, 555–570.
196. Newhall, S. M.   The constancy of the blue arc phenomenon.   *J. opt. Soc. Amer.*, 1937, **27**, 165–176.
197. Newhall, S. M.   Measurement of simultaneous contrast.   *Psychol. Bull.*, 1940, **37**, 500.
198. Newhall, S. M.   Preliminary report of the O.S.A. subcommittee on the spacing of the Munsell colors.   *J. opt. Soc. Amer.*, 1940, **30**, 617–645.
199. Newhall, S. M.   Warmth and coolness of colors.   *Psychol. Record*, 1941, **4**, 198–212.
200. Newhall, S. M.   Chapters 4 and 5 in O.S.A. Committee on Colorimetry, *The Science of Color.*   New York: Thomas Y. Crowell Co., 1953.
201. Newhall, S. M., and J. G. Brennan.   The I.S.C.C. comparative list of color terms.   Inter-Society Color Council, 1949.
202. Newhall, S. M., R. W. Burnham, and J. R. Clark.   Comparison of successive with simultaneous color matching.   *J. opt. Soc. Amer.*, 1957, **47**, 43–56.
203. Newhall, S. M., R. W. Burnham, and R. M. Evans.   Influence of shadow quality on color appearances.   *J. opt. Soc. Amer.*, 1959, **49**, 909–917.
204. Newhall, S. M., and R. Dodge.   Colored after images from unperceived weak chromatic stimulation.   *J. exp. Psychol.*, 1927, **10**, 1–17.
205. Newhall, S. M., D. Nickerson, and D. B. Judd.   Final report of the O.S.A. subcommittee on the spacing of the Munsell colors.   *J. opt. Soc. Amer.*, 1943, **33**, 385–418.
206. Nickerson, D., and W. C. Granville.   Hue sensibility to dominant wavelength change and the relation between saturation and colorimetric purity. *J. opt. Soc. Amer.*, 1940, **30**, 159–162.
207. Nickerson, D., and S. M. Newhall.   A psychological color solid.   *J. opt. Soc. Amer.*, 1943, **33**, 419–422.
208. Nickerson, D., and D. H. Wilson.   Munsell reference colors now specified for nine illuminants.   *Ill. Eng.*, 1950, **45**, 507–517.
209. Oberlin, K. W.   The relative immediacy of sensory, perceptual, and affective characteristics.   *Amer. J. Psychol.*, 1930, **42**, 621–625.
210. Odbert, H. S., T. F. Karwoski, and A. B. Eckerson.   Studies in synesthetic thinking: I. Musical and verbal associations of color and mood.   *J. gen. Psychol.*, 1942, **26**, 153–173.
211. Otero, J. M., L. Plaza, and F. Salaverri.   Absolute thresholds and night myopia.   *J. opt. Soc. Amer.*, 1949, **39**, 167–172.
212. Parsons, J. H.   *An introduction to the study of colour vision.*   Cambridge: The University Press, 1915.
213. Peckham, R. H.   An objective study of binocular fusion.   *Amer. J. Psychol.*, 1936, **48**, 474–479.

214. Pickford, R. W. A practical anomaloscope for testing colour vision and colour blindness. *Brit. J. physiol. Optics*, 1957, 14, 2–26.

215. Piéron, H. Des lois d'établissement du chroma des impressions lumineuses. *Comptes Rendus, Académie des Sciences*, Paris, 1929, 189, 194–197.

216. Piéron, H. L'Évolution de la sensation lumineuse. *Amer. J. Psychol.*, 1937, 50, 23–32.

217. Piéron, H. Les spécificités chromatiques dans la latence des impressions lumineuses. *Revue d'Optique*, 1949, 28, 157–160.

218. Pillsbury, W. B., and B. R. Schaefer. A note on 'advancing and retreating colors.' *Amer. J. Psychol.*, 1937, 49, 126–130.

219. Pinegin, N. I. Absolute scotopic sensitivity of the eye in the ultra-violet and in the visible spectrum. *Nature*, 1945, 155, 20–21; 1944, 154, 770.

220. Pirenne, M. H. Binocular and uniocular threshold of vision. *Nature*, 1943, 152, 698–699.

221. Pitt, F. H. G. The effect of adaptation and contrast on apparent brightness. *The Proceedings of the Physical Society*. London: 1939, 51, 817–830.

222. Planta, P. von. Die Häufigkeit der angeborenen Farbensinnstörungen bei Knaben und Mädchen und ihre Feststellung durch die üblichen klinischen Proben. *v. Graefes Arch. Ophthal.*, 1928, 120, 253–281.

223. Polyak, S. L. *The retina*. Chicago: University of Chicago Press, 1941.

224. Polyak, S. L. *The vertebrate visual system*. Chicago: University of Chicago Press, 1957.

225. Pope, A. *Art, artist and layman*. Cambridge (Mass.): Harvard University Press, 1937.

226. Pope, A. Notes on the problem of color harmony and the geometry of color space. *J. opt. Soc. Amer.*, 1944, 34, 759–765.

227. Porter, T. C. Contributions to the study of flicker. *Proceedings of the Royal Society*, 1902, B70, 313–329.

228. Priest, I. G., and F. G. Brickwedde. The minimum perceptible colorimetric purity as a function of dominant wave-length. *J. opt. Soc. Amer.*, 1938, 28, 133–139.

229. Purdy, D. McL. On the saturations and chromatic thresholds of the spectral colors. *Brit. J. Psychol.* (*General Section*), 1931, 21, 283–313.

230. Purdy, D. McL. Spectral hue as a function of intensity. *Amer. J. Psychol.*, 1931, 43, 541–559.

231. Purdy, D. McL. The Bezold-Brücke phenomenon and contours for constant hue. *Amer. J. Psychol.*, 1937, 49, 313–315.

232. Rand, G. The factors that influence the sensitivity of the retina to color: A quantitative study and methods of standardizing. *Psychol. Monogr.*, 1913, No. 15, 166 pp.

233. Riggs, L. A., F. Ratliff, J. C. Cornsweet, and T. N. Cornsweet. The disappearance of steadily fixated visual test objects. *J. opt. Soc. Amer.*, 1953, 43, 495–501.

234. Ross, R. T. Studies in the psychology of the theater. *Psychol. Rec.*, 1938, 2, 127–190.

235. Sanders, C. L., and G. Wyszecki. Correlate for lightness in terms of CIE-tristimulus values. Part I. *J. opt. Soc. Amer.*, 1957, 47, 398–404.

236. Sanders, C. L., and G. Wyszecki. L/Y ratios in terms of CIE-chromaticity coordinates. *J. opt. Soc. Amer.,* 1958, **48,** 389–392.
237. Sanders, C. L., and G. Wyszecki. Correlate for lightness in terms of CIE-tristimulus values, Parts I and II. *J. opt. Soc. Amer.,* 1957, **47,** 398–404 and 840–842.
238. Sawyer, R. A. *Experimental spectroscopy* (2nd Ed.). New York: Prentice-Hall, 1951.
239. Schober, H. *Adaptation of vision at night through use of red light and red spectacles.* U.S. Department of Commerce, Washington, 1946.
240. Schouten, J. F., and L. S. Ornstein. Measurements on direct and indirect adaptation by means of a binocular method. *J. opt. Soc. Amer.,* 1939, **29,** 168–182.
241. Schrödinger, E. Grundlinien einer Theorie der Farbenmetrik im tagessehen. *Ann. der Physik,* 1920, **63,** 397–426, 427–456, 481–520.
242. Sears, F. W. *Optics.* Cambridge (Mass.): Addison-Wesley Press (3rd ed.), 1949.
243. Ségal, J. *Le mécanisme de la vision des couleurs.* Paris: G. Doin & Co., 1953.
244. Sheard, C. Dark adaptation: Some physical, physiological, clinical, and aeromedical considerations. *J. opt. Soc. Amer.,* 1944, **34,** 464–508.
245. Sheard, C. The effects of smoking on the dark adaptation of rods and cones. *Proceedings of the Federation of the American Society of Experimental Biology,* 1946, **5,** 94.
246. Silberstein, L. A fundamental criterion of uniform representability of equiluminous colors on a geometrical surface. *J. opt. Soc. Amer.,* 1942, **32,** 552–556.
247. Sloan, L. L. The effect of intensity of light, state of adaptation of the eye, and size of photometric field on the visibility curve, a study of the Purkinje phenomenon. *Psychol. Monogr.,* 1928, **38,** No. 1, 87 pp.
248. Sloan, L. L. A quantitative test for measuring degree of red-green color deficiency. *Amer. J. Ophthal.,* 1944, **27,** 941–947.
249. Sloan, L. L. Rate of dark adaptation and regional threshold gradient of the dark-adapted eye: Physiologic and clinical studies. *Amer. J. Ophthal.,* 1947, **30,** 705–720.
250. Washburn, M. F., and D. L. Smith. Stereoscopic binocular fusion in the original impression and in the negative after-image. *Amer. J. Psychol.,* 1933, **45,** 320–321.
251. Southall, J. P. C. *Introduction to physiological optics.* New York: Oxford University Press, 1937 (pp. 387–388).
252. Stainton, W. H. The phenomenon of Broca and Sulzer in foveal vision. *J. opt. Soc. Amer.,* 1928, **16,** 26–39.
253. Staples, R. The responses of infants to color. *J. exp. Psychol.,* 1932, **15,** 119–141.
254. Staples, R., and W. E. Walton. A study of pleasurable experience as a factor in color preference. *J. genet. Psychol.,* 1933, **43,** 217–223.
255. Steinhardt, J. Intensity discrimination in the human eye. I. The relation of $\Delta I/I$ to intensity. *J. gen. Physiol.,* 1937, **20,** 185–209.
256. Stevens, S. S. The relation of saturation to the size of the retinal image. *Amer. J. Psychol.,* 1934, **46,** 70–79.

257. Stevens, S. S.   Mathematics, measurement, and psychophysics.   Ch. 1 in S. S. Stevens (*Ed.*) *Handbook of Experimental Psychology.* New York: John Wiley & Sons, Inc., 1951.

258. Stiles, W. S.   The effect of glare on the brightness difference threshold. *Proceedings of the Royal Society,* 1929, **B104,** 322–351.

259. Stiles, W. S.   A modified Helmholtz line-element in brightness-colour space. *Proc. Phys. Soc.,* 1946, **58,** 41–65.

260. Stiles, W. S.   Separation of the 'blue' and 'green' mechanisms of foveal vision by measurements of increment thresholds, *Proceedings of the Royal Society,* 1946, **B133,** 418–434.

261. Stiles, W. S.   The determination of the spectral sensitivities of the retinal mechanisms by sensory methods.   *Ned. T. Natuurk,* 1949, **15,** 125–146.

262. Sumner, F. C., and F. P. Watts.   Rivalry between uniocular negative after-images and the vision of the other eye.   *Amer. J. Psychol.,* 1936, **48,** 109–116.

263. Swindle, P. F.   Positive after-images of long duration.   *Amer. J. Psychol.,* 1916, **27,** 324–334.

264. Taylor, I. L., and F. C. Sumner.   Actual brightness and distance of individual colors when their apparent distance is held constant.   *J. Psychol.,* 1945, **19,** 79–85.

265. Tennant, J.   The psychological factor in colour contrast.   *Brit. J. Psychol.,* 1929–1930, **20,** 1–26.

266. Tessier, M., and F. Blottiau.   Variations des caractéristiques photométriques de l'oeil aux luminances photopiques.   *Revue d'Optique,* 1951, **30,** 309–322.

267. Thouless, R. H.   Phenomenal regression to the real object, I.   *Brit. J. Psychol.,* 1931, **21,** 339–359.

268. Thurstone, L. L.   *Multiple factor analysis.*   Chicago: Univ. of Chicago Press, 1947.

269. Torgerson, W. S.   *Theory and methods of scaling.*   New York: John Wiley & Sons, Inc., 1958, Chap. 11.

270. Troland, L. T.   The colors produced by equilibrium photopic adaptation. *J. exp. Psychol.,* 1921, **4,** 344–390.

271. Troland, L. T.   *Psycho-physiology,* Vol. II.   New York: Van Nostrand Co., 1930, p. 181.

272. Tyndall, E. P. T.   Chromaticity sensibility to wave-length difference as a function of purity.   *J. opt. Soc. Amer.,* 1933, **23,** 15–24.

273. Tyndall, E. P. T.   Sensibility to wave length difference as a function of purity.   *J. opt. Soc. Amer.,* 1927, **14,** 137.

274. Venkataraman, K.   *The chemistry of synthetic dyes,* Vols. I, II.   New York: Academic Press, 1952.

275. Waaler, G. H. M.   Über die Erblichkeitsverhältnisse der verschiedenen Arten von angeborener Rotgrünblindheit.   *Acta ophthal, Kbh.,* 1927, **5,** 309–345.

276. Walls, G. L.   *The vertebrate eye.*   Bloomfield Hills, Michigan: The Cranbrook Press, 1942.

277. Walls, G. L.   The filling-in process.   *Amer. J. Optom. & Arch. Amer. Acad. Optom.,* 1954, **31,** 329–340.

278. Wallach, H.   Brightness constancy and the nature of achromatic colors. *J. exp. Psychol.*, 1948, **38**, 310–324. See Ref. 86.

279. Walraven, P. L., H. J. Leebeek, and M. A. Bouman.   The I.S.C.C. color aptitude test.   The interpretation of some testing results.   Rep. No. WW1956-10.   *Instituut voor Zintuigfysiologie R.V.O.-T.N.O.*   17 pp.

280. Walton, W. E., and B. M. Morrison.   A preliminary study of the affective value of colored lights.   *J. appl. Psychol.*, 1931, **15**, 294–303.

281. Walton, W. E.   The sensitivity of children and adults to color harmony. *Psychol. Monogr.*, 1933–34, **45**, 51–61.

282. Washburn, M. F., and S. L. Grose.   Voluntary control of likes and dis-likes; The effects of an attempt voluntarily to change the affective value of colors.   *Amer. J. Psychol.*, 1921, **32**, 284–289.

283. Washburn, M. F., D. Haight, and J. Regensburg.   The relation of the pleasantness of color combinations to that of the colors seen singly. *Amer. J. Psychol.*, 1921, **32**, 145–146.

284. Washburn, M. F., K. G. McLean, and A. Dodge.   The effect of area on the pleasantness and unpleasantness of colors.   *Amer. J. Psychol.*, 1934, **46**, 638–640.

285. Wells, F. L.   Reactions to visual stimuli in affective settings.   *J. exp. Psychol.*, 1925, **8**, 64–76.

286. White, H. E.   *Introduction to atomic spectra.*   New York: McGraw-Hill Book Co., Inc., 1934.

287. White, H. J., Jr. (Ed.).   *Proceedings of the Perkin Centennial.*   New York: American Association of Textile Chemists and Colorists, 1957.

288. Willis, M. P., and D. Farnsworth.   Comparative evaluation of anomalo-scopes.   *New London, Med. Res. Lab. Rep.*   No. 190, 1952, 89 pp.

289. Wolf, E.   Effects of ultraviolet radiation on visual thresholds.   *Science,* 1947, **105**, 366.

290. Woods, W. A.   *The color aptitude test.*   Sparta, N.J. (Box 318): Color Division, Industrial Psychology Laboratory, 1952.

291. Woodworth, R. S., and H. Schlosberg.   *Experimental psychology.*   New York: Henry Holt & Co., 1954.

292. Wright, W. D.   *Researches on normal and defective colour vision.*   St. Louis: The C. V. Mosby Co., 1947.

293. Wright, W. D.   *The measurement of colour* (2nd Ed.).   London: Hilger and Watts, Ltd., 1958.

294. Wright, W. D., and F. H. G. Pitt.   Hue discrimination in normal colour vision.   *Proceedings of the Physical Society*, 1934, **46**, 459–473.

295. Wyszecki, G., and C. L. Sanders.   Additional studies of the correlate of lightness in terms of CIE-tristimulus values.   *J. opt. Soc. Amer.*, 1957, **47**, 338.

296. Wyszecki, G., and C. L. Sanders.   Correlate for lightness in terms of CIE-tristimulus values.   Part II.   *J. opt. Soc. Amer.*, 1957, **47**, 840–842.

Index